HEALING

At Any Price?

Samuel Pfeifer M.D.

HEALING
At Any Price?

WORD PUBLISHING

Word (UK) Ltd
Milton Keynes, England

WORD AUSTRALIA
Heathmont, Victoria, Australia
STRUIK CHRISTIAN BOOKS (PTY) LTD
Salt River, South Africa
ALBY COMMERCIAL ENTERPRISES PTE LTD
Balmoral Road, Singapore
CONCORDE DISTRIBUTORS LTD
Havelock North, New Zealand
JENSCO LTD
Hong Kong
SALVATION BOOK CENTRE
Malaysia

ISBN 0–85009–153–5

Typesetting by Suripace Ltd, Milton Keynes.
Reproduced, printed and bound in Great Britain for Word (UK) Ltd
Cox and Wyman Ltd, Reading.

93 / 10 9 8 7 6 5

CONTENTS

FOREWORD

There can be little doubt that our generation has entered a new era of medicine. The modern emphasis on wholistic health is a welcome one but it has brought with it both blessings and dangers. How do we find our way through the maze of conflicting ideas and assumptions that surround the subject of alternative medicine - a field in which so many seem to be more committed to the end than to the means? What position do we as Christians need to take in relation to the symptom-relieving remedies which appear to work yet bring about strange reverberations in our spirits?

Dr Samuel Pfeifer has come to our assistance with a book which in my opinion is destined to become one of the most informative books on the subject of alternative medicine that has yet been written. As a minister and a counsellor I have longed for some time to be able to put into the hands of those who write to me with questions concerning the subject of alternative medicine, a book that would give them the perspective they need. Although there are many fine articles, features and booklets on various aspects of this subject written by committed Christians, I know of nothing that compares to the depth and treatment which Dr Pfeifer has given to the issue. He writes not only from a background of medical understanding and experience but from a deep commitment to the Scriptures. One senses that his aim in every chapter is not just to impart understanding but to glorify the Lord.

I warmly commend this book not only to the great army of counsellors, doctors, nurses and so on, for whom it will have special interest, but also to those individuals who, facing continued sickness, may easily find themselves drawn to remedies that do not glorify the Lord. May God use this most significant book to deepen understanding and give protection to His people.

Selwyn Hughes
Founder and Director
Crusade for World Revival

To Annemarie

INTRODUCTION

HOLISTIC HEALTH is becoming increasingly popular. With its emphasis on the wholeness of mind, body and spirit, it is especially attractive to those who are looking for an alternative approach, many of whom are Christians. There seem to be so many positive aspects to this New Medicine, such as its emphasis on humanism and spirituality, that not only patients, but increasing numbers of doctors are being attracted to it.

Medical school has taught us to read electrocardiographs and to interpret X-rays, but it has not adequately prepared us to deal with the patient as a whole. It is very difficult to teach such things as listening skills, empathy, and how to penetrate a smoke screen of presenting symptoms. It is even more difficult to teach values and spiritual truths to a generation of scientists who have been raised with an exclusively materialistic world view.

This emptiness and therapeutic helplessness made me very open to alternative methods of healing. When I was in Medical School, I became fascinated with acupuncture, and even prepared an outline for a seminar which made the Chinese needle art palatable for Christians.

Why did I believe in it? I was swept away by the persuasive propaganda campaign of the early seventies: it was new, it was natural, it worked. News magazines published enthusiastic articles and TV programmes featured it. A Chinese professor gave us a lecture bestowing on acupuncture the blessings of science. My spiritual and scientific discernment was washed away like a sandcastle by the tide.

As time went on however, I became increasingly aware that the alternative healing methods of the New Age had philosophical overtones that could not be easily brushed aside. A *Festival of Mind , Body and 'Spirit'* in London, and later in Los Angeles, featured the following interest areas (as quoted from the official programme):

- Natural Health and Beauty
- Spiritual Well Being
- Natural Therapies and Healing.
- Fitness, Yoga and Meditation
- Ecology and Environment
- Psychic Phenomena
- UFO's and Ancient Mysteries
- Health Foods
- Astrology, Tarot and Clairvoyance
- Nutrition and Diet
- Alternative Technology
- Music, Dance, Singing

I realised that Holistic Health was much more than a spiritually neutral model of alternative healing!

How was it possible that so many Christians were undergoing treatment from Holistic Health practitioners without questioning their spiritual background? It may be because some of the methods do not seem outrightly occult. There are few doubts about the demonic nature of black magic, Satanism and psychic healing. But the kingdom of darkness has a twilight zone which is equally dangerous. Many a patient has already become hopelessly lost by turning to obscure methods in his quest for healing.

But what about the validity of acupuncture and reflexology, homoeopathy and iridology, radiesthesia and other unconventional healing methods? Aren't there scientific proofs that they actually work? Isn't there a neutral way to use them? Isn't it true that: "If it works, it's O.K."? Or can occult bondage and oppression result from these less obviously occult practices?

It was not easy to find answers. Christian doctors and counsellors very often had not thought the problem through and were unable to give specific guidelines. Similarly, Christian literature only yielded scattered hints.

So I started my own research, reading every possible publication on the subject. I talked to healers and their patients, to acupuncturists and homoeopathists, herbologists and parapsychologists. This book is the result of my investigations.

I have tried to look at the subject from as many angles as possible. What are the changes in our society that have caused us to seek New Age hopes? What are the philosophical roots of these new methods? How were these practices discovered and developed? Are there scientific studies on the therapeutic value of a given technique? How do we distinguish the apparently natural aspects of a method from its underlying Eastern-Mystical elements?

I have selected those practices which most clearly reveal the twilight zone between light and darkness. More or less neutral methods, such as most conventional diets or hydrotherapy, are not examined here. It is not my intention to compile a comprehensive catalogue of all alternative healing methods. Neither is it my intention to classify every healer spiritually, philosophically or scientifically. Rather I hope to give the reader some guidelines which might help him to discern the spirits for himself. The same principles found here would also apply to similar practices not specifically mentioned.

There is definitely a spiritual message woven into "Holistic Health", a message that cannot be ignored any longer. The so-called "miracles" of alternative medicine are preparing the way for further deception such as the future world religion mentioned in the Bible. It is my conviction that the things in this world are intimately tied to unseen spiritual realities. Healing "miracles" with such overt religious overtones will undoubtedly have their side-effects on the mental and spiritual well-being of the patient.

However, this book is more than just a sombre warning. It is my hope that it will make you aware of lasting spiritual values. Too often we Christians have made the same mistake we criticise in materialistic science; separating the physical and spiritual, soul and body. We need to adopt a new perspective of sickness and health based on the light of the Bible. Avoiding alternative healing methods with their roots in mysticism and occultism does not simply leave us alone in "the clutches of modern medicine" with its one-sided emphasis on the physical. I am convinced that the Bible, the Word of God, does have important answers that can give us new confidence and hope. Meeting the Almighty God through Jesus Christ will not only have a positive effect on our spiritual life but on our whole being: spirit, soul and body.

Sam Pfeifer M.D.

One

In the Clutches of Modern Medicine?

Without modern medicine, life in our Western world would be inconceivable. Today, virtually every baby is born in a hospital, and two out of three people die in a hospital bed, often surrounded by intravenous lines, wires, bleeping computers, flickering cardiac monitors and a host of other machines - a frightening scenario.

Afraid of hospitals

More and more people are becoming afraid of hospitals. A building without a soul; a nightmare of concrete, glass and fluorescent lights - that's what many people think of the place which is supposed to help them, where concern and care are expected most.

Anxiety is triggered by the mere smell, that peculiar scent of sterility, so characteristic of hospitals. People's anxiety is heightened by the sight of other patients with limbs in plaster, I.V. bottles and drawn faces. Everyone initially feels that gnawing uncertainty: "What will they find wrong with me? What tests will I have to endure? Will it hurt? Will I ever be able to leave this place again?"

Soon the patient finds himself dressed in his anonymous white hospital gown. And although he entered walking, he is now being moved in his bed through endless corridors, from one test to the next.

A door opens. His bed is pushed into a dim room: a strange hum fills the air. Little coloured lights flicker in a dark corner. Nobody tells him what the "thorax" is that they want to "take". Gradually he begins to recognise the silhouette of a huge machine as well as tubes and cables hanging from the ceiling above, modern technical substitutes for the ancient sword of Damocles. In his fear, the waiting time stretches into an eternity. The thin second-hand on the big clock seems to creep at a snail's pace from one line to the next . . . Finally an X-ray technician comes in. She helps him out of bed, shows him how to stand - click, click - and the chest film is taken. It was not that bad, after all!

While he is waiting for the next test in some corridor, all those recent headlines he has seen whizz through his mind: "human guinea-pigs", "hospital without feeling", "malpractice: doctors in court", "unnecessary operations", "operation successful - patient dead".

The image of modern medicine, as press reports depict it, is scary indeed. Often one case is singled out, stripped of its complexity and presented as a gripping horror-story. Medicine seems to be in the headlines only when something goes wrong. Rarely are there reports about the hundreds of satisfied patients, the thousands of successful operations, and the healing effect of many drugs.

On the other hand, we have to be careful not to cover things up. When there is malpractice and neglect, we should not shruggingly accept the situation. We have to recognise the problems brought in by modern science with its lopsided understanding of man. For too long, body and soul have been torn apart, resulting in the restoration of physical health while spiritual and psychological needs remain neglected. For too long, also, modern medicine has been placed on a pedestal and viewed with unrealistic expectations.

Does the hospital make people sick?

Hospitals do not only bring healing; in many cases they also make people sick. This was shown in various studies; "The healing process may be protracted and endangered," says a psychologist, "by unnecessary periods of waiting, delays in meeting needs, and by fears or feelings of hopelessness at being at the mercy of the doctors."

Conversations with the doctor often contribute to a patient's anxieties. According to various studies, a junior hospital doctor only spends an average of 1.7 - 3.7 minutes talking with each patient on his daily rounds. All too often I have witnessed how doctors were more interested in lab-results and ECG's than in the questions and requests of the patient. In their conversations they mumble unintelligible Latin-Greek expressions that the patient does not understand and from which he draws the most horrible conclusions on the state of his health.

Even worse still, the diagnosis may replace the patient's name, or he may be written off as a "psycho" or a "hopeless case". In his room he might be known as the "endocardial myofibrosis," the "gastric C.A.," the "irritable colon," or simply "the old chap near the window".

Medicine, in spite of its claims of helping and healing , is increasingly finding itself caught in a crossfire. French comedian Molière's one-line catch phrase seems more and more accurate: "Most people die from their medicines and not from their diseases". And modern day medical critic Dr. Robert Mendelsohn puts this warning on his book *Confessions of a Medical Heretic*: "Caution: Medicine as practised in America today may be dangerous to your health!"

Worse than before

It can really happen that a patient fares worse after treatment than before. For example: a 50-year old businessman consulted his family doctor complaining of pain in the hip. He was treated with a shot of cortisone. One day later the injection site started swelling, and a bright-red warm and very painful lump developed - an abscess caused by a contaminated needle. In the hospital he was first admitted to the medical department, where doctors hoped to cure him by pumping him full of high doses of antibiotics. Two days later, the whole leg became red and swollen, as a result of the abscess spreading downwards. He was then transferred to the surgeons, who in a long operation, had to open up the entire leg to evacuate the pus. It was about two months before the patient could leave the hospital. He was left with a stiff hip covered with ugly scars

- all because of one injection!

In medical terminology this is what is called "iatrogenic disease" (iatrogenic = caused by the doctor). Ivan Illich, the best known and most radical medical critic, regards the effects of modern medicine as "one of the fastest-growing epidemics on our planet". Illich, who is not a physician himself, exaggerates by far, but it cannot be denied that there is a grain of truth in his allegations.

Unnecessary operations

Many operations are really unnecessary. Under the slogan, "If in doubt, cut it out," many surgeons display a rather generous inclination to operate, to say the least. According to a large U.S. study (as quoted in Illich's *Medical Nemesis*), of the 787,000 surveyed operations to remove the uterus , 173,000 (22 per cent) were unnecessary. Similarly, the authors regarded as not indicated: 14 per cent of all gall-bladder operations, 29 per cent of prostatectomies, and a high 70 per cent of all tonsillectomies. The frequency of appendectomies seems to vary considerably from one country to another. In Germany, surgeons remove the appendix three times as often as in other European countries. "That peculiar disease," remarks professor of social medicine Dr. Pflanz, that occurs only rarely on weekends, and hits white collar workers three times more often than labourers." Microscopic examinations of the removed segments showed that the operations had been unnecessary in two thirds of the cases.

But if one is familiar with the difficulties of an exact diagnosis of appendicitis, one becomes more careful in passing judgement. It is safer to remove ten appendices unnecessarily than to see one patient die from peritonitis.

Even worse than unnecessary operations is therapeutic shoddiness and malpractice, which is being increasingly dragged into the limelight by the media. "Operation successful - patient dead" - thus ran the headline in a tabloid, dramatically describing the sequel to an operation on a 16-year old student. The orthopaedic surgeon had fixed his broken collar-bone with a wire. After the surgery, one wire-end looped into the chest and pierced the pulmonary artery and the boy's heart. He expired after ten days from internal bleeding.

Tragic cases like this one are a macabre paradox, being a welcome source of income for a host of specialised lawyers. Like hyenas some of them linger around hospitals trying to solicit "customers". In the United States, one out of every seven surgeons is currently facing charges of malpractice. Huge sums of money are usually involved, (rarely is a suit filed for less than one million dollars), much of which is being siphoned off into the pockets of the various experts and attorneys, only a fraction being left for the patient himself,

These law-suits do not necessarily contribute anything to more personalisation of care or cost-effectiveness in the medical system. Many American doctors would rather pass the scene of an accident than risk a law-suit for malpractice. Many lab-tests are done unnecessarily simply to protect the doctor, or a hospital, from a possible law suit. It comes as no surprise that US health expenditures in 1980 totalled 224.6 billion dollars, compared with only 136 billion dollars in US defence spending or India's gross domestic product of a modest 117.6 billion dollars in the same year.

Pills instead of talk

Automatic laboratory equipment and computerised diagnostic gear are increasingly replacing the personal contact with the physician. A patient from the US came to Zurich to see one of my professors who was a world renowned expert in internal medicine. The patient carried with him a list of no less than 89 lab results, from haemoglobin to exotic enzymes such as the serum: fructose-1,6-diphosphate-aldolase.

Lack of communication deprives the modern doctor of the chance to detect early those numerous complaints which are not uncovered by the most advanced medical gadgetry. Instead of an understanding conversation patients receive plenty of medication. If you happen to spend three weeks in a hospital you will be treated with an average of nine to ten different medicines, and if you are admitted to a University medical centre, you may even be given (with your "informed consent") drugs yet in their experimental stage. Patients who are entered as guinea-pigs in a "controlled study" are often subjected to more, as well as unnecessary blood-tests, X-rays and other investigations.

Whilst some journalists have gone to the extreme of using the red-flag word "human experiments" alluding to the Nazi horrors, it is a fact that too many medical research studies are conducted to gain reputation or money and not to meet a need. On the other hand there will never be medical progress without finally testing a new drug or treatment in human test-persons, after potential risks have been monitored in animal studies. And still there is that uncanny feeling deep down . . .

Yearning for new medicine

If we take into account the rising fear of modern technical medicine, we will be better able to understand the widespread yearning for an alternative medicine; a medicine that spares people the "horrors" of the hospital, where they get therapy without huge medicines, drugs without side-effects, and healing without surgery.

And that's exactly what they are promised by health practitioners and psychic healers. Here they can finally receive the longed-for human contact. There are no unintelligible expressions, no complicated Latin diagnoses. Their disease is explained in a simple context that anyone can grasp. For example, it may be the electrical balance of the body, or the solar plexus that is disturbed. The practitioner may claim that there are scars disturbing the smooth flow of a patient's vital energy, or that the reflex zones of a patient's feet have been neglected. Every reader of illustrated magazines and tabloids is familiar with these concepts. The prescribed herbal remedies and biological juices are natural and do not have any side effects. At least that is the conclusion of the medical layman. These issues are obviously not that clear-cut, and we will deal with some of them in later chapters..

One of the greatest hopes for a patient is the possibility of avoiding an already scheduled or advised operation. Naturopaths stress the fact that one in seven operations is unnecessary and give remarkable and peculiar advice on how to prevent surgery: vegetarianism cures cancer of the breast and avoids mastectomy, acupuncture clears your abscesses without aspiration, injections of oxygenated blood prevent the amputation of a smoker's leg, homoeopathic remedies can spare you from thyroidectomy, and self-hypnotic imaging techniques will conquer cancer.

Thus what begins as a healthy scepticism or fear of modern day medicine, ends as a wandering search for alternative methods of healing. More and more patients are losing their confidence in Western medicine. They are buttressed even by some medical doctors who have turned into advocates of Holistic Health. Dr. Mendelsohn, for example, gives his patients this advice when dealing with their doctor: "What you are to do, is turn around, and put as much distance between you and him as you can, as fast as your condition will allow." And the author of a book on psychic healers tells his readers: "If you want to be healed, don't trust your doctor!"

Where, then, does one turn? Is there a better way?

* * * *

In this chapter I have deliberately described the image of modern medicine as it is rendered in many publications by the press. Personally I could not discard the whole of modern medicine in such a crass and general way. Although I am very critical of some of the extreme aspects of technical medicine I am thoroughly convinced that many doctors and nurses in the hospitals do genuinely care about the well-being of their patients. Complications occur comparatively rarely and it will never be possible to avoid them completely.

By describing only the mistakes and problems, the critics have completely misinterpreted the real achievements of modern medicine, without which none of us would really like to live.

In talking to many sick and healthy people, I have realised that the seed of fear and mistrust sown by the critics of modern medicine is springing up in their hearts. The consequence is a desperate search for alternatives. The alternatives in themselves are not without dangerous side effects, as we shall see in future chapters.

Two

The Bio-Boom

BOSTON, JANUARY 23rd. A Superior Court judge today ordered the parents of Chad Green, a 3 year old leukaemia victim, to stop treating him with what physicians call "metabolic therapy", which the doctors said was poisoning the child.

Laboratory tests. . . showed there was evidence of cyanide poisoning in Chad, which medical authorities attributed to the use of laetrile and heavy doses of vitamin A. A previous court order denied Chad's parents, Gerald and Diana Green of Scituate, Mass. the right to prevent their son from undergoing chemotherapy prescribed by physicians . . .

(New York Times, January 24, 1979).

Because they regarded chemotherapy as poison, the parents of Chad Green put their hope in nutritional therapy. By feeding him a special diet that avoided meat, white sugar, white flour, preservatives, and artificial colourings and flavourings, and consisted largely of fresh fruits and vegetables, fish, cheese, goat's milk and distilled water, plus vitamin and mineral supplements, they thought they could protect Chad from "the toxic effects of chemotherapy". They later stopped giving him his prescribed medication altogether. When the leukaemia recurred, the doctors finally appealed to the court in order to help save Chad's life. The family eventually fled the country, continuing the therapy with laetrile and diet, until the boy died about a year later.

This story is typical of our time, in which we are witnessing a veritable bio-boom, as a reaction to the seeming helplessness of scientific medicine.

50,000 medications - 50,000 side-effects

A landmark study by the National Center for Health Services Research shows that 60 per cent of all Americans bought at least one prescription drug in 1977 - pills and capsules in all colours and shapes, ointments and lotions, powders, drops or suppositories. Whereas in 1930 the British Pharmaceutical Industry sold medicines worth 12 million pounds, in 1980 its sales exceeded 2 billion pounds.

Today there are about 50,000 different medications available. But the assumption that they can heal most diseases is painfully wrong: only one third of the diseases currently known can be treated by drugs which influence the underlying cause. The lack of effective drugs is especially obvious in the group of killer diseases like cancer, arteriosclerosis and heart disease, where doctors are still looking for therapies which not only relieve symptoms, but cure the underlying process.

There are about as many side-effects as there are drugs. The computer centre of the World Health Organisation in Geneva has registered about 50,000 side-effects of prescription drugs since it came into existence in 1968. Every year three billion dollars are spent in the United States to treat the consequences of drug side-effects. Even the most popular, aspirin, (annual consumption in the United States: 20,000 tons) causes a respectable list of 31 undesired side-effects, ranging from simple skin rashes to stomach ulcers. Whereas most incidents of undesired drug side-effects have little consequence, about 20 years ago the tranquillizer thalidomide led to a catastrophe: thousands of children whose mothers had taken the drug during pregnancy, were born deformed and handicapped for life.

Tranquillizers, such as valium and librium, have almost become a symbol of our affluent Western society. They account for 30 per cent of the pharmaceutical industry's sales. In Britain, one out of ten night's sleep is induced by a sleeping pill.

As long ago as 1975, a White House drug abuse task force reported that seven to eight million Americans were abusing amphetamines, barbiturates and tranquillizers prescribed by doctors. The number of "prescription junkies" is increasing every year.

Cracks in the temple

In reaction to this chemical invasion is a growing movement that rejects "toxic chemistry". Many people are disillusioned with science and are increasingly feeling the threat of uncontrollable consequences. As a result, they are turning their backs on their former god with an abruptness that was inconceivable only a decade ago.

People are voicing the same concern in different ways: the environmentalists in Maine, USA prevented the construction of a huge water project because it would have endangered a rare plant in that area. Farmers in Europe beleaguered an aluminium plant with their tractors, carrying black flags to protest against pollution of the air. The opponents of nuclear power plants have used political slogans and violent riots to make known their protests. The fanatical crowds of Ayatollah Khomeini toppled the Shah not only for religious reasons but also because of his fast-paced and forceful industrialisation of the predominantly rural country.

"The hopes for a happier future," says German physician and author Hoimar von Ditfurth, "have given way to the anxious fears of an over-populated, polluted and increasingly repressive world".

For decades scientists and the media have preached the optimistic view that one day, with the help of human reason, all problems could be solved. But now the temple of science is slowly decaying, like the ancient Greek sanctuaries of the Acropolis in Athens. The cracks in the walls cannot go unnoticed, and no one is sure when the roof will cave in. Modern priests with their test tubes and computers have proved unable to fulfill the hopes of mankind for a new, better world.

Tanaland is ruined

German psychology professor, Dr. Doerner, some years ago conducted an extremely interesting experiment underlining the fact that man is not able to solve the world's problems with intelligence and technology. Twelve students from different faculties were given the power, in computer simulations, to improve the living conditions of the Tupi and Moro tribes. The tribesmen were existing on the brink of famine in the African developmental area "Tanaland".

The advisers had dams built, irrigation systems installed, forests cleared and fields fertilised; they hunted wild animals and sprayed insecticides. But the result of all their efforts was shattering. Idi Amin could not have ruined the country in worse fashion.

Despite all their knowledge, for they were all highly intelligent, they were unable to foresee the long-range results of their measures, nor could they calculate the possible detrimental side-effects. They killed the monkeys which caused damage to the plantations, but did not realize that the leopards, having lost their usual prey, would then go after the cattle.

Tanaland is everywhere: when man disturbs the ecological systems, catastrophes follow sooner or later. The floods that are afflicting northern India in ever increasing severity have their cause in the destruction of huge forest areas in the mountains which had previously absorbed the water. One of the worst time bombs ever set by man is the insecticide DDT, which for two decades was the number one weapon against all sorts of pests. In their report on *The Limits of Growth*, scientists of the "Club of Rome" have demonstrated how DDT, even decades later, has accumulated in fish. Tests have shown DDT concentrations in mothers' milk that are far beyond the legal limits. Fortunately it take comparatively high doses of DDT to cause toxic effects in humans, whereas one hundredth of a millionth part of one gram is deadly to a fly.

Nevertheless, more and more people are bothered by aerial spraying of fruit plantations and forests with highly effective insecticides and consequently, housewives are willing to pay a higher price for apples that have been grown without any chemicals.

Sales slogan "biological"

The adjective "biological" has become a sales slogan with magical attraction. Everything is "natural". Cosmetics have a "natural affinity", "Nature's Gate" is advertised as "the purest, most effective beautifying conditioner your hair will ever know", and herbal tea is supposed to be better when it is "organically grown, hand harvested and sun dried". There are dozens of "natural" breads available; for example, the "stoneground 100% whole wheat bread, sweetened with molasses and honey, no preservatives added!" You do not have to give up hamburgers if you want to eat healthily, because now "Nature's Burger Fills the Void". And for bio-conscious smokers there is "Honey-rose, the Alternative Cigarette", a mixture of the "traditional smoking herbs", Ginseng and honey. The prices are sometimes outrageous. One brand of brown sugar goes for seven times the price of white sugar, although it is no less detrimental to the teeth.

Rather a curiosity among biological products is the "negative ion pump Energen" which offers you the following advantages:

> Now you can control the environment - continuously recycle, purify, cigarette smoke and odours - stimulating increased energy, alertness and exhilaration. The Hybrid Energen system "digests" the polluted air, purifies it and releases it back to you - refreshed and revitalised - with an abundance of negative ions.

This trend is especially lucrative for health food stores and producers of "natural products" and vitamins. The Bio-Boom has led to a multi-billion dollar business. "Bioforce Inc." for example, a Swiss-based company producing herbal remedies and teas blended according to the prescription of a local healer and herbalist, has seen a 40 per cent annual growth despite the economic recession. Over the last few years the company founded no less than ten affiliated firms in Scandinavia, the Netherlands, the United States, Canada, Australia and South Africa.

Self, Self, Self

The Back-to Nature trend has also found its expression in the bookshops. Diet manuals are flooding the market, from "nutritional therapy" to "Macrobiotics", which is inspired by Taoist philosophy. Lavishly illustrated books on ecology and the preservation of nature are selling by the hundred thousands. British author John Seymour has written a manual, *The Complete Book of Self-Sufficiency*, for those who are fed up with the rat race life in our polluted cities and want to escape to the countryside. The book soon made its way into the top ten best-sellers list.

But here we have touched on a key-word that emerges time and again, and that should cause us to pause and think with regard to the bio-wave. There is one word that continually reverberates in the movement: the term *"self"*: self-efficiency, self-realisation, self-healing, self-hypnosis and so on. Man has realised that science and technology cannot fill his needs. But instead of turning to God, "the giver of all good things", people are looking for salvation within themselves.

The New Age man is ready "to repent" in his own way, by turning his back on the exploitation of nature and health. He is willing to accept the loss of a meaningful relationship with established society, especially the medical establishment. He is ready to change his life to adhere to strict diets, to meditate for hours, or to take a stand in demonstrations against nuclear weapons. His new gods are nature, his health, and his ego. His new goals are the realisation of his human potential, harmony with cosmic energies, the attainment of a renewed balance of polar forces within himself and, ultimately, unity with the universe.

From a Christian viewpoint, all these efforts are avoiding

the cure of the human dilemma, man's relationship to his one true Lord, and are straying towards the deception of Eastern philosophy and cosmic humanism. "On the altars purged of the big old gods," writes Hoimar von Ditfurth, "there are now appearing many little idols."

Three

The Occult Revival

We live in an area of occult revival. What seemed impossible only a decade ago has become commonplace in our days. What was rejected as superstition, sorcery and spiritism by the average person only a few years ago, has now become acceptable through science and parapsycology.

A definition

As the terms "occultism" and "magic" will be used repeatedly in this book, let me give a short definition of their meaning (adapted from Leslie A Shepard, *Encyclopedia of Occultism and Parapsychology*, Detroit: Gale Research Co, 1978).

Occultism (from Latin *occultum* = the concealed) denotes a philosophical system of theories and practices on and for the attainment of the higher powers of mind and spirit. Its practical side connects with psychical phenomena.

Magic (from Greek *magikos*): a practice based on the laws of *sympathy* (like cures like: e.g. a stone called bloodstone can staunch the flow of bleeding, *antipathy* (the application of an object expels its contrary), and *contiguity* (whatever has once formed part of an object, continues to have an invisible bond to it. Thus, the possession of a hair of a person allows a sorcerer to diagnose and heal sickness over distance).

In a stricter sense magic is the art of producing extraordinary and wonderful effects that cannot be explained by man's normal capacities. To produce magic phenomena, contact is sought with impersonal "cosmic energies" or directly with personal spirits. In Deuteronomy

18:10-12 the Bible clearly condemns these practices as an "abomination" to God.

More astronomers than physicists

Newspapers without a daily horoscope have become rare. Whereas thirty years ago only a few American papers carried an astrological column, today 1200 of the nation's 1750 dailies provide their readers with a horoscope. A poll in West Germany revealed that 45 per cent of adults believe in the possibility that there is a connection between the position of the stars and their human destiny. In Europe and the United States there are three times as many registered fortune tellers and astrologists as there are chemists and physicists. They are not only consulted by uneducated people but by executives, company directors, administration officials and politicians. You might smile at the official astrological consultants of the political leaders in far-away India. You'd better make sure that the politician you have voted for has not consulted a fortune teller to explore his political chances. Fortune telling has become a multi-million dollar business.

Dungeons and Dragons

It is alarming to find occult games being advertised as ideal gifts for children, such as the *Ouija-board*, or games like *Clairvoyant*, *Horoscope*, *Kabbala* or *Voodoo*.

One such new game is called *Dungeons and Dragons*. Magic circles, pentagrams and thaumaturgic triangles are incorporated into the game - items all used in black magic and witchcraft. Within the game players are encouraged to worship Tlazoleotl (the goddess of vice), Lu Yeuh (the god of epidemics) and Azathoth (the centre of the universe). In a magazine that corresponds to the game - *Deities and Demigods* pp, 36, 40 and 44 - it clearly says, "Those who worship Azathoth worship insanity". Encouragement is given for the players to "fantasise together", and to "summon supernatural forces". This kind of involvement can hardly be less than consulting a medium, who in turn consults "familiar spirits". Inevitably this will have its own effect on those who get involved.

Even at the first level of the game, those who play are learning about casting spells, extrasensory perception, levitation, evil spirits (the undead), ghouls, mediums and blasphemous reference to "other gods" - Rulebook p.15. Children are encouraged to imagine monsters, werewolves and so on - and fear is the prime element in the "fun". In the early stages the game does make its appeal to fantasy, but in view of all the foregoing it needs to be asked where it is all leading. Many evil things have begun in an apparently harmless way.

Music is not exempt. In the realm of rock music, Heavy Metal groups in particular are composing songs dedicated to the devil. Many of the record album covers have on them pictures full of occult symbolism and signs. As well as the words of the songs, many of the records have messages recorded in reverse on them - back masking. These messages, many of them related to devil worship, get through to the sub-conscious, and these begin to exert their influence on the individual.

Table tapping, hypnosis and contacting spirits through a medium have become widespread party-games. Clairvoyants are employed to solve criminal cases, such as Peter Hurkos who assisted police in 17 countries to clear up murders.

Telepathy in the submarine

Telepathy is being used in places where you would not anticipate it. Because the army wants to utilize the occult technique as a means of communications for submarines, parapsychology has been declared a state secret in the Soviet Union. Even the American navy, in 1959, conducted experiments in telepathic communication with the atomic-driven submarine *Nautilus*. When *Apollo 14* was on its way to the moon, American astronaut Captain Edgar Mitchell made telepathic experiments. Although nothing to do with the *Apollo* project, these experiments have given respectability and acceptability to the paranormal phenomenon in the eyes of many people.

The number of Americans who are involved in sorcery, satanism and black magic is estimated at around 10 million. Britain has about 8000 practising witches from all levels of society and they are organised in "convents". In the area between Rome and Milan alone there are 10,000 magicians and fortune-tellers. France has more psychics, fortune-tellers and astrologers than Catholic priests.

In 1966, the first official church of Satan was founded. Its high priest, Anton LaVey, says: "The Satanic Age started in 1966. That's when God was proclaimed dead, the Sexual Freedom League came into prominence, and the hippies developed as a free sex culture". His *First Church of Satan* is one of the fastest growing churches in California. In 1969, only three years after its foundation, it boasted 6000 members.

However, not only Europe and the United States are witnessing this boom in occultism. In Brazil the African Macumba and Umbanda cults are claiming a membership of 30 million. The Umbanda cult is officially recognised as a religion. In this largest Roman Catholic country of the world, the openly spiritistic cult of the Karecists is supported by one million adherents. In large gatherings, they worship the spirits of the dead. Their number is growing fast, especially among the socially underprivileged in the big cities. They have lost their faith in both a corrupt regime and a traditional church, and are now looking to the high priests of the Satanic cults to bring them happiness, salvation and healing.

The Hollywood spectacle *The Exorcist* was probably the single most important trigger for the occult invasion into the mass media. What was once practised in the dim light of a candle is broadcast today into millions of homes. Where there were once a few hundred people flocking to see a magician at the vaudeville theatre, today millions succumb to the suggestion of Uri Geller.

Marketing the occult

The occult explosion has also hit the bookshops.

Hundreds of occult books are being published every year and are reaching mindboggling sales, from Carlos Castaneda's books on sorcery to the astrological guides for Virgo, Leo or Aquarius, from the Tibetan Book of the Dead to the increasing occult literature of Thanatology. Even respected publishers are taking their chances to make money with the occult. Humanistic philosophy and cosmic transcendentalism do not seem to exclude one another any more.

It is not surprising, therefore, that people become increasingly ready to believe in extrasensory realities. Science fiction literature is not merely entertainment but has become the pacemaker of a new attitude towards the unseen world. The heroes of *Star Wars* are protected and guided by a good "power". Steven Spielberg's films such as *Close Encounters of the Third Kind* are having such obviously religious overtones that one critic speaks of a "substitute religion".

"Presently, superstition is attaining a new, almost medieval boom," writes a magazine. "With a vehemence unimaginable only a decade ago, people - even intellectuals - have turned their backs on the once highstrung expectations of science: the disillusioned of the scientific age are rediscovering the mysticism of Hermann Hesse, of Zen Buddhism or Transcendental Meditation."

Psychic healing in the Philippines ...

The new superstition, however, is not limited to ESP in space and technology. To an ever increasing degree, people are ready to expect *healings* from methods that not only lack any scientific foundation but obviously rely on psychic powers.

Every year thousands of patients from the West are making their pilgrimage to Baguio, a small town in the Philippines where they are having their diseases operated on by psychic healers who work with their bare hands and no scalpel. Witnessing such an "operation" is extremely impressing for a medical layman: the healer gently strokes the area over the stomach. Suddenly, blood wells up and is carefully wiped away by an assistant. Now the "surgeon" delves into the cavity and soon presents a bloody something, "the ulcer", as he describes it to the patient. One minute later (the duration of a real stomach operation being two hours and more) the blood is wiped off, the skin closed without a scar, and the operation is over. The patients are enthusiastic about the quick and painless operation, and many of them feel much better for some time.

A closer look at the healings reveal a completely different picture: microscopic and biochemical examinations of the "removed" tissue have shown that they were entrails of chickens, dogs, rats and pigs. The blood on one patient's cotton swab was identified as pig's blood at the Forensic Institute of the University of Zurich.

In his excellent book *Healing: A Doctor in Search of a Miracle*, the American surgeon W.A. Nolen has described very vividly what tricks these healers are using to deceive the psychic believers from the West. Nonetheless, parapsychologists are clinging to their explanation that the operation is carried out on the patient's "energy body". "I am convinced," says one of them in an interview with a large Swiss newspaper, "that the existence of the energy body will be recognised in the West, within the next 10 or 20 years."

... and in the West

You do not have to travel as far as the Philippines to witness patients who willingly submit to a healer who promises to heal them with the help of magical powers. In January 1982 I had the opportunity to attend the *Festival of Mind, Body and Spirit* in Los Angeles, where dozens of healers were demonstrating their art. I will never forget the patients sitting there with closed eyes and folded hands, expecting a miracle to happen, while a healer laid hands on them.

The "laying on of hands" is no more confined to some obscure psychics. The New York Times reports:

An unorthodox therapy in which

> nurses attempt to make sick patients feel
> better by 'laying hands' on them is being
> introduced in hospitals and nursing
> schools throughout the country.
>
> In many ways similar to the laying on
> of hands that is practised by faith healers
> and mystics . . . the therapy is taught at
> graduate level by Dr. Dolores Krieger. . .
>
> (6 November 1977).

How closely related these practices are to Eastern
mysticism is revealed by a quotation from the *Nursing
Forum*: "Whether it be called *prana* or an aura or magnetic-
fielding, that therapeutic 'something' which transfers from
one loving person into another is what Jesus called the
power of God."

The training is part of the increased influence that the
Holistic Health movement is having on the medical
profession. Doctors and nurses are not immune any more
against the massive occult wave that's overrolling them. A
poll among 500 German physicians revealed that only 27.4
per cent of them did not in some way use unorthodox forms
of treatment. Most of them are probably using Holistic
techniques because they want to spare their patients the
negative side effects of more dangerous medications. The
overall tendency is obvious, however: as they increasingly
experience frustrations with a one-sided materialistic
approach, more and more doctors are seeking refuge in
obscure therapies. Over 1500 physicians in Germany
practise acupuncture, more than 1000 homoeopathy; in
France the figures are similar. In Britain about 1600 "psychic
healers" have the official permission to treat patients under
the National Health system. The number of doctors who
recommend Yoga, Zen and Transcendental Meditation for
relief of stress, cannot be estimated.

Especially among younger physicians there is a growing
openness towards the occult. I know of several physicians
who studied medicine with me, and who have since joined
occult orders, attended spiritualistic seances or have been
initiated into TM.

Holistic Health Conferences, sponsored by the Californian Mandala-Society and the American Medical Student Association, among others, are attended each year by over 3000 health professionals and educators for their professional credit. Lecture topics in 1982 included: *Meditation: Changing our Mind and Transforming our World; Science and Human Potential; Hypnosis and Healing* or *Our Latent Powers: Discovering and Developing for Health, Healing and Pain Control.*

Physicians guarantee the success of acupuncture, and prove, without the help of expensive and sophisticated instruments, the healing effects of Transcendental Meditation. Physicians are checking their diagnosis with the help of Iridology or a Radionic pendulum.

There is much talk today of a "neutral" application of healing methods that have their roots in the occult. A scientifically trained doctor is readily taken as a guarantee for "clean" Holistic treatment. But the above cited examples underline the fact that the title of an "M.D." cannot be taken as a security that an otherwise occult technique is applied in its "neutral, scientific" form, and is therefore without side-effects on the psychological and spiritual well-being of the patient.

Four

Acupuncture - Healing Needles from the East

The American professors are stunned. There they stand by invitation of the Chinese government, in one of the modern operating theatres at the Peking Medical College.

The bright lights are focused on a man in his fifties, lying there on the table. A team of surgeons gather round the patient. An acupuncturist steps forward and injects the patient with a small dose of morphine at an acupuncture site near the jaw. This acts as a tranquillizer. Then she carefully swabs the patient's left forearm with alcohol and inserts a needle between the wrist and the elbow. Gently the needle is moved up and down and to and fro between the doctor's fingers. After about twenty minutes, the patient says he feels the typical sensation of heaviness and numbness in the areas around the needles. The acupuncturist signals the surgeon to go ahead.

The scientists, each one a well-known specialist in his field, look on incredulously as the surgeon swiftly makes a 14-inch incision running from the spine across the left side of the chest to the patient's breastbone. Then, with a scissors-like instrument, he cuts away two ribs and inserts a chest retractor to spread open the rib cage, and there lies the rosy lung, softly moving up and down with the rhythm of the patient's breathing. Most amazing: during the whole operation, which is one of the most difficult we know, the patient keeps up a steady stream of banter with his doctor. At one point the operation is interrupted so that he can eat some fruit. Throughout the whole procedure the acupuncturist is steadily manipulating the needle in the patient's arm. Recalls one of the American doctors: "The patient didn't jerk, move or sweat. He did nothing to indicate pain or discomfort".[1]

Since 1971, when this took place, reports of the Chinese needle miracles have remained in the news. Acupuncture has since become a respectable research topic in Western universities and even today, scholars do not agree on how it works or why it works. Among the medical institutions involved in doing acupuncture research are Boston's Massachusetts General Hospital, the University of California Medical Center and the Institute of Rehabilitation and Medicine in New York.[2]

The unsolved mystery

Acupuncture, however, is not only applied to alleviate pain. More and more naturopaths and acupuncturists are using it successfully to heal all sorts of ailments, from hayfever to duodenal ulcers, from sweaty feet to drug withdrawal. More than 1000 acupuncturists are practising in France alone and about 1500 in Germany, with their numbers increasing throughout the Western world. New forms of acupuncture are being "invented" almost every year. In acupressure, for example, the pressure of the fingers substitutes for the needles. In laser-acupuncture a fine laser beam is employed. Ear-acupuncturists claim that all the needle sticking points have their equivalent in the ears, thus making whole-body-acupuncture unnecessary, and finally, in electro-acupuncture the needles are connected to an electrical control box which generates electrical vibrations.

All these methods are based on the principles of Chinese acupuncture. Some of the different schools are involved in bitter contentions about "the right way" to practise the art,[3] a quarrel we shall come back to later in this chapter.

Despite all the stories of success, it is still not clear how acupuncture really functions. In the years 1976 and 1977 alone more that 100 scientific articles were published in respectable medical journals, in which the authors tried hard to explain how it worked - for example a golden needle in the ear could reduce the discomfort caused by varicose veins.

What should our attitude as Christians be regarding

acupuncture? Does it have only its name in common with Chinese acupuncture? Or is it a new form of hypnosis, bringing patients under the influence of demonic powers? To what extent is a doctor's or naturopath's practice of acupuncture affected by its obvious Eastern roots?

I will try to shed light on these questions by analysing how Western acupuncturists view their therapy, and by considering the experiences of various Christian counsellors who have dealt with patients who have been treated by acupuncture.

The Yellow Emperor's Classic of Internal Medicine A short history of acupuncture

Chinese medicine is very ancient. The foundations of the empire's traditional healing art may be traced back to the legendary Emperor Huang Ti who lived about 5000 years ago. His teachings were handed down through the centuries by oral tradition and finally written down in *Huang Ti Nei Ching Su Wen*, the *Yellow Emperor's Classic of Internal Medicine*.

This book described the discussions of Huang Ti with his chief minister and a doctor on the functions of the human body, as well as its diseases and their healing. The whole work is inspired by the astrological and religious concepts of their time. For the Western reader it is as unintelligible and mysterious as the vast country beyond the great Chinese Wall itself.

It was the goal of Huang Ti and medical writers in China to integrate the function of man with the functioning of the universe. The five elements that constituted the world were correlated to five solid organs: the heart, lungs, kidneys, liver and spleen. Each of them corresponded to a hollow organ: the large intestine, small intestine, gall bladder, stomach and bladder.

These organs stood in a strange relationship of amity and adversity to one another, reflecting the qualities of the five elements: wood, fire, earth, metal and water. The kidneys as organs of water were the enemy of the heart which was the organ of fire. Each organ was also correlated with a planet and a season of the year. For example the heart had a correlation with summer.[4]

Most important, however, were the effects of the life energy "Chi" with its components of Yin and Yang which permeated all creatures. This "cosmic spirit" was said to circulate throughout a complicated system of numerous channels, called meridians.

Because the dissection of the human body was prohibited for religious reasons, the Chinese had only vague ideas of human anatomy. Whereas the brain was thought of as a small insignificant organ, the spleen was regarded as the centre of reasoning.[5] Whatever they lacked in knowledge, they made up for in a complex theory of correlating Yin and Yang to the various organs. Thus the back was Yang, the front Yin. The liver, heart, spleen, lungs and kidneys were Yang, while the stomach, gall bladder, large and small intestines and the bladder were Yin. Yang was the symbol of warmth, strength and masculinity. Yin, on the other hand, stood for coldness, weakness and femininity.

The "Magic Gate"

The second part called the "Magic Gate", or the "Nei Ching", describes the actual ways an acupuncturist may heal and prevent diseases. Besides a thorough description of the needling points, it includes a multitude of herbal recipes and various forms of massage as well as magic spells and charms.[6] All these methods were supposed to restore the balance of cosmic forces in the patient. It was the theory of the first part, and the practical applications of the second part of the "Nei Ching" which formed the fundamentals of traditional Chinese medicine.

As in other ancient cultures, medical knowledge in China rested in the hands of the priests . This was demonstrated by the discovery of bones bearing etched-in texts dealing with various diseases.

"The description of such ailments etched into oracle-bones shows how ancient Chinese medicine was governed by the idea that diseases were sent by gods and demons".[7]

Obviously the treatment with needles, later termed acupuncture (from the Latin *acus* - "needle" and *punctus* - "point") in the West, goes back to the earliest doctors, probably spiritistic shamans. They performed rituals similar to those found in today's Voodoo-cults, that attempt to expel evil spirits by sticking needles into the body of the sick.[8] Later scholars abandoned the demonic model and integrated the use of needles into their astrological theories.[9]

Chinese healers did not only develop their own forms of therapy, they also had their own way of diagnosing diseases. They looked for external signs of internal processes. "Accidental observations led to the assumption of a relationship between the outward appearance of the tongue or the eye and internal diseases."[10] These led to a whole diagnostic system, based on speculation and vivid fantasy rather than on reality. The parallels with modern systems of unconventional diagnosis, such as iridology (see chapter 7), are striking. Most important in the Chinese system was "pulse-diagnosis", "as the pulse was also a link in the great conception of man and cosmos".[11] Later, we will refer in greater detail to this practice.

Acupuncture did not always enjoy the same popularity in China through the centuries, but it remained an important element within the framework of traditional Chinese medicine. Roman Catholic missionaries of the Society of Jesus were among the first to bring acupuncture to France, about 200 years ago. During the French Revolution acupuncture was a very fashionable treatment. However, it lost its popularity in ensuing years,[12] even though there are places such as the Paris hospital "Hôtel Dieu", where patients still line up for acupuncture sessions. Medical insurance in France will cover the application of acupuncture if it is performed by a doctor and if other therapies have been unsuccessful.

Before we look into the practice of acupuncture in the West, let's have a closer look at the philosophical underpinnings of acupuncture, primarily Taoism.

Harmony with the universe

Taoism is an ancient Chinese religion, dating back to the legendary philosopher Lao-Tse. "It scintillates in all colours," writes one commentary, "and contains elements of philosophical Taoism. . .combined with the relics of traditional religion, sorcery, geomancy and alchemy."[13]

Long before Lao-Tse there had been speculation in ancient China about a natural force that had generated the universe. This cosmic energy was called Tao and its varied manifestations were explained by the polar forces of Yin and Yang.

"The term *Tao* from which the religion derives its name," writes sinologist and former director of the China Inland Mission, Dr. Leslie Lyall, "is the same word used to translate both 'the Word' in Chapter 1 and 'the Way' in Chapter 14 of John's Gospel. The term is of great importance to Chinese thought. It means primarily the 'way' or the 'road' and thus 'the way of the universe'. It is supposed to be the first principle, even preceding God - the 'universal cosmic energy behind the order of nature'."[14]

The Tao has two faces, Yin and Yang. They are opposed to one another and yet still one. In contrast to Biblical teaching, Taoism does not distinguish between the opposing forces of light and darkness, God and Satan. Good and Evil come from the same source. "The Chinese," says Marcel Granet, an expert in Chinese philosophy, "neither see an absolute contradiction between religion and magic, nor between pure and impure."[15] Such a teaching is called "monism" (from Latin *mono*, one) and it is a basic assumption in all Eastern religions as well as in modern Holistic therapies. It is no surprise to find it in Chinese medicine: "Chinese medicine understands man as one in body and spirit, a complete unit, finding its ultimate harmony only in Tao."[16]

"This universe is filled with oscillations between the activities of Yin and Yang," writes a Taoist philosopher of our time.[17] "All of the beings and phenomena which appear and disappear are nothing but multiple and varied aggregates of these activities which issue from the primordial cosmic energy of the Infinite Expansion. Everything is a metamorphosis of this One Infinity, containing various proportions of Yin and Yang."

Yin and Yang have a relationship with star constellations, the basic elements (fire, wood, water etc), the seasons, colours, our emotions, and the functions of our bodies. Chinese philosophers try to create complex systems which integrate all these interactions.[18] They divide the body into eight parts each having its own symbol. These symbols are composed of short and long lines arranged in three layers on top of one another, called *trigrams*. Used by the ancient masters of the oracle for psychic diagnosis, they now reappear in modern books of acupuncture.

The primary concern of Taoist philosophy is *harmony between man and the universe.* Man is subordinate to the authority of heaven and the power of the Tao and therefore compelled to live a virtuous life. The Chinese philosophers were convinced that *macrocosm*, the infinitely large world of the heavens and nature, exercised influence on *microcosm*, the miniature world of the human body. At the same time microcosm influenced macrocosm. The emotions, inner organs, virtues and elements are interrelated with the cosmic energy, "Ch'i", which permeates the whole universe and man. Thus the enlightened one who studies the correlation between body openings and inner organs gains comprehensive knowledge about heaven and earth.

Immortal through meditation?

Lao-Tse could have been a prophet of today's counter-culture; he opposed science and culture, seeing solutions only in a return to a natural and simple lifestyle. Many Taoist hermits and ascetics tried to prolong their lives by meditation and a retreat into nature. Life-elixirs and immortality pills were produced with the help of alchemy, radiesthesia, magic and mysticism. He who had unconditional *faith* in those remedies was promised success with them.

A legend tells the story of a believer who first tried an immortality pill on his dog who expired shortly after.

Undaunted, he still took the pill in faith - and died. His brother fared no better, but when the youngest brother wanted to bury their bodies, they not only woke up to live again, but received immortality as a reward for their unwavering faith.[19]

Another element of Taoism is *meditation*. Through its practice people have to attain a spiritual body, sublime beyond all restrictions of this world. Physical and spiritual discipline is practised in order to extinguish the ego that will eventually be replaced by the all-embracing power of Tao. Having attained this goal, nothing in the world could darken the external bliss. One could walk through walls, ride on clouds, and command spirits and demons at will.[20]

Health and invincibility through meditation - don't these words remind you of the promises of Maharishi Mahesh Yogi and his programme of transcendental meditation? Times may change, the programmes may sound different, but again and again occult prophets promise to man the things he dreams of.

"But what has a man profited if he gains the whole world and loses his own soul?"

No acupuncture without Eastern philosophy

The occult background of acupuncture is played down by many of its modern practitioners. This is illustrated by Dr. J. Bischko, a Viennese acupuncturist, who maintains that the Chinese were "not a mystical people, on the contrary, they were pronounced realists. However, they were masters at accomplishing their will on earth by referring to higher powers. Thus, they consulted water diviners to find out if the planned site for a house was agreeable to diverse spirits. In reality these people were skilled landscapers. . ."[21]

With this attitude it is not surprising to learn that acupuncture "research" is conducted with the radionic pendulum, among other methods, at the Ludwig-Boltzmann Institute at Vienna which is headed by Dr. Bischko.[22]

Other acupuncturists have completely turned their backs

on Taoist philosophy, the mother of their art. "Forget about the teachings of Taoism," I was told by an acupuncture doctor. "What we do with our needles is in reality the stimulation of the autonomic nervous system. The ancient Chinese have ingeniously recognised these systems and integrated them into their philosophical teachings for lack of better knowledge."

I have encountered this view especially among scientifically trained physicians. They do not want to deny a certain effect, but on the other hand, try to keep away from superstition and occultism.

What is down-played by some and explained away by others, is fiercely defended by a third group. The amazing effects of acupuncture can be reached "only when the practitioner follows the principles handed down through the millenia," declares acupuncture-specialist Dr. Schnorrenberger.[23] He even rejects the combination of Western diagnosis and Chinese treatment. Never should Western acupuncturists choose their needling sites according to scientific Western medicine. "It is absolutely necessary," he writes, "that acupuncturists follow the theories of ancient Chinese medicine, if they want to see significant success. If they disregard these ancient theories, then they can only practise an unspecific stimulation therapy at best."[24] Similar statements have been made by modern Taoist philosopher George Ohsawa, the father of Macrobiotics. He expressly states that *oriental medicine cannot be separated from its philosophical underpinnings.*[25] Many parapsychologists and psychics, therefore, regard acupuncture as a proof of their occult teachings. And more and more people are believing them, swept away by the overwhelming flood of positive reports in the media.

Pulses, points and meridians

As we have seen, acupuncturists do not even agree among themselves. Before we go into further details, let's have a look at some of the concepts they work with:

1. the energy Ch'i   2. the meridians

3. Yin and Yang   4. the acupuncture points
5. the diagnosis   6. the therapy

Then let us listen to some researchers who have conducted in-depth studies of these areas. Are there *scientific proofs* for the claims of acupuncture?

A little later on we will discuss the theories commonly used to explain *how acupuncture works*. Is it possible to demonstrate any lasting effects of acupuncture? Why is it effective with patients in Western hospitals, for instance for pain relief? And finally we will turn to the question: Are there *occult elements* affecting the modern practice of acupuncture, and if so, where are they found?

1. The energy Ch'i

"The root of acupuncture is in the spirit...the human spirit is endowed from heaven. The physical energy is endowed from the earth". This is how an ancient Chinese manuscript describes the situation.[26]

We have already seen that the primordial cosmic energy plays a central role in Chinese thinking. The energy permeating the human body and emanating from the infinity of the universe is called "Ch'i". Every invisible power, be it the rolling of thunder, the flashing of lightning, the moving of an arm or the growth of a flower, is traced back to Ch'i.

Similar concepts can be found in Hindu philosophy which calls the life-energy "prana". Prana reveals itself in the universe, but has its seat in the heart of man. Some psychics call themselves "pranic-healers" as they are relying on this energy for healing.[27] There are other names for this force. Some call it "ethereal body", and some healers know it as "vital life energy".

According to Chinese theory, the Ch'i of the body is received from the Ch'i of the air. From there it enters the respiratory system which is in turn connected to the large intestine. The stomach, on the other hand, filters Ch'i out of the food and passes it on to the spleen.

Man can only function properly when his Ch'i is in harmony with the cosmic energy. A woman can only conceive when she lives in universal harmony. Decreasing Ch'i weakens the body and death occurs when the Ch'i escapes from the body.

2. The Meridians

Energy, according to Chinese sages, circulates in defined vessels, called "meridians". These are not identical to nerves, arteries, veins or lymph vessels. The body is supposed to have twelve meridians, each corresponding to a different organ. There is a heart meridian and a gall bladder meridian, a lung and a large intestine meridian, and so forth. Each one is assigned a shorthand name which consists of a combination of letters and numbers. Special functions are ascribed to the meridian with the flowery name "triple warmer". It is supposed to influence three functions: respiration, nutrition and sexual potency. In addition to the twelve meridians arranged in pairs there are two "wonderful vessels", called the "governing vessel" and the "vessel of conception". They contain many important acupuncture points.

The vital force pulsates through these meridians in a certain cosmic rhythm; thus each meridian has times of maximal energy level and times of energy depletion. The "master of the heart" is most susceptible between noon and 2 p.m. and the liver meridian between 2 and 4 a.m. All these rhythms have to be taken into consideration if the acupuncturist wants to treat a patient properly.

3. Yin and Yang

The polarities of Yin and Yang play an important role in Chinese philosophy. In the same way that nature oscillates between Yin and Yang, so does the vital force in the human body. As long as these forces are in balance, the energy Ch'i can flow.

Disease is caused by an imbalance of Yin and Yang. According to this principle Emperor Huang Ti described the terrible fever attacks of malaria as follows:

The chill and fever are due to the
alternating replacement of Yang and Yin.
The phenomenon is brought about by the
heat in summer. This heat is stored up
beneath the skin and will manifest itself in
the form of chills and fever at other
seasons when the Yang and Yin lose their
state of counterbalance.[28]

For the physician trained in Western medicine, it is very
difficult to trace a disease back to the purportedly guilty
meridian. For example, a Yin/Yang imbalance in the spleen
meridian may cause the following symptoms: nausea,
stomach pains, hiccoughs, indigestion, insomnia, a craving
for sweet-tasting foods, fatigue during the day, diarrhoea,
or a general feeling of illness. Affections of the small
intestine meridian are said to cause deafness, yellow eyes,
pain in the elbow, pain in the neck, or swelling in the face.[29]

4. The Acupuncture Points
There are over 700 needle points located along the
meridians. Acupuncturists distinguish different types:
vitalising and sedating points, welling and streaming
points, heralding and consenting points, reunion and
cardinal points (according to Bischko).[30] To find tiny points
measuring between 1-3 millimetres, acupuncturists use a
punctoscope. Basically it measures skin resistance by lighting
up when it touches an area with lowered resistance. The
scientific value of these complicated-looking gadgets is very
questionable.

5. The Diagnosis
Chinese medicine recognises four types of diagnosis:
1. Wang = observation
2. Ting = listening and smelling
3. Wen = inquiring
4. Tsie = pulse diagnosis

When an acupuncturist uses *observation* he does not look
for pathology as a Western physician would, although he
seems to use a very similar procedure. He observes the

body's openings, especially the tongue and the eyes. The eyes are regarded as the outlet of the liver, with the upper lid giving information on the spleen and the white of the eyes showing the condition of the lungs. The procedure is an early predecessor of modern iridology which we will deal with in depth in chapter 7.

Through *listening* and *smelling* the acupuncture practitioner gathers further important details. Not only does he notice the vibration of the voice, but he also tries to detect subtle aromas, which help him to find the centre of a Yin/Yang imbalance. Today's cosmetic industry is certainly complicating this part of his work!

The emphasis is also different from Western medicine when the Chinese doctor explores the patient's history by *inquiring*. In his enquiry, the practitioner not only wants to know the geographic location where a patient lives but he also wants to know about his climatic conditions, his food, his activities and his daily rhythm, as the stars and planets have an important influence on all these areas. All questions refer to Yin and Yang thus giving information on his condition.

These ancient diagnostic methods are used in a variety of ways by modern acupuncturists in the West. Some have abandoned them completely and prefer to rely on scientific tests of blood, stool and urine. Others insist that only the Chinese way can give the leading clues for correct treatment.

Especially controversial, in the Western camp of Huang Ti's followers, is the most important tool of Chinese analysis: *pulse diagnosis*. The pulse is much more to the acupuncturist than simply the heart beat. In it he feels the vibrations of the patient's cosmic energy, giving him the best indication of his condition.

He takes the patient's right hand at about the same location as Western physicians would, and puts three fingers on the wrist. At first he barely touches it with his fingertips, thus feeling the "superficial" pulses which tell him about the functions of the large intestines, the stomach and the "triple warmer". Then he increases his pressure to find the "deep pulses" giving him details on the condition of lungs, spleen and sexuality. To examine the remaining six organs regarding their energetic level, he feels the pulses of the left hand.

Commenting on the method, acupuncturist Stiefvater[31] writes: "Pulse diagnosis, in my opinion, brings the subconscious of patient and healer in touch with each other. . .The whole procedure suggests an archaic method of exploring, via the pulse, the complex mind-body relations which the Chinese called Ch'i (energy). There are possibly sensitive examiners who are *able to tap the subconscious of their patients in this way*". (Italics mine).

6. The Therapy

After having established the diagnosis, be it through ancient or modern methods, the acupuncturist starts the treatment. Western acupuncturists work with a set of the following needles, the length of which varies between 1.5 and 7 inches.[32]

- 2 golden facial needles (purportedly vitalising)
- 2 silver facial needles (purportedly relaxing effects)
- 2 long gold needles
- 4 small gold needles
- 4 long silver needles
- 6 small silver needles
- 2 Japanese needles (from silver or steel)

Again, there is much latitude, and there are therapists who work with an entirely different set. There are controversies as to the necessity of using gold or silver needles, and debate as to whether the same effects can be brought about with needles simply made of steel.[33,34] Opinions are divided among experts on how many needles to use. While photos showed pin-cushion-like heads a few years ago, only relatively few needles are applied in the current use of acupuncture.

It is the goal of therapy to re-establish the disturbed balance of Yin and Yang and thus to cure the illness.

Where does acupuncture promise help?

What are the diseases that can be treated or cured according to acupuncturists? The following list was presented in an address by French acupuncture specialist Dr. deTymowski:[35]

1. All forms of pains, especially due to rheumatic conditions, tendon-inflammations, neuralgias, migraine, shingles or post-operative pain.

2. Spastic conditions, such as stomach and intestinal spasms, constipation, diarrhoea, gastric and duodenal ulcers.

3. Paralytic conditions, such as polio and paraplegia (!) during the rehabilitation stage.

4. Sleep disturbances.

5. Bed wetting.

6. Allergies, including hayfever, eczema, asthma and itching conditions.

7. Mild forms of depression and anxiety neurosis.

8. Varicose veins and haemorrhoids.

9. Fractured bones following accidents and operations (accelerated healing claimed).

10. Certain types of hearing and speech disorder.

11. Alcoholism, cigarette and drug dependence/addiction.

The list given here is slightly abbreviated, but is a classic example of the exaggerated claims of acupuncture cures. It is criminal to give paraplegics hope from acupuncture, especially as no cure has been demonstrated and neither has there been any convincing result in the treatment of deafness.[36]

So much now for the statements of acupuncturists. But how do they support their claims? To what extent can their explanations prove true in controlled scientific studies? Is acupuncture really fulfilling the high expectations it is arousing? Why is it not working with every patient? Is the needling technique really all that natural and safe? These are just a few questions requiring further clarification.

Shaky proofs

Many physicians who practise acupuncture feel somewhat uncomfortable with the philosophical and occult heritage implied in their profession. Again and again they try to vindicate and explain their therapy. Thus the German Academy for Acupuncture Inc. rejects every explanation implying "heaven and earth" or "disordered energies".[37] Dr. Johannes Bischko, Director of the Ludwig Boltzmann Institute in Vienna, however, does not want to be so extreme. Although he too tries to demystify acupuncture, he would like to retain the concepts, "as they go far beyond our narrow definitions of corresponding synonyms".[38] And the reason for the intensive research into acupuncture by the Chinese lies in the fact that the communist rulers want to purge the mystical background out of it. It just does not fit into their materialistic worldview.

As Bischko defines "cosmic energy" simply in terms of changes in the electrical field of the earth, researchers at his Institute work hard to demonstrate these electrical energies. One of his co-workers, physicist Maresch (who, by the way, also uses radionic devices to explore unconventional therapies) has examined skin reactions under different weather conditions. Using highly sensitive measurements of cutaneous resistance, he detected points with an especially low resistance, and these were purportedly identical with the traditional acupuncture points.[39]

As has already been mentioned, this same method is used in everyday practice to "find" the sticking points. Doubts about this method have been voiced by experts in the field, such as Dr. G. Fisch who made numerous measurements and found them to be unreliable.[40]

As a matter of fact, *skin resistance* depends on multiple factors having nothing to do with acupuncture. What is actually measured with these devices is merely the sweat-excretion of the patient.[41] Needless to say every person will react with increased sweating when he is pricked with a needle! But that does not prove that there are specific acupuncture points. Skin resistance has been used in *psychology* to measure a test-person's emotional reaction to a certain image, and also to investigate the impact of TV commercials on the consumer.[42] Skin resistance tests are also used in criminology in the form of lie detectors. If a suspect, during cross examination, is caught in a web of lies he will inadvertently start to perspire more intensively, indicating to the examiner that he is uncomfortable at this point. An attempt to demonstrate the existence of acupuncture points was made by Austrian histologist G. Kellner. An histologist is someone who examines tissues using a microscope. He examined 12,000 specimens of skin that had been punched out of recently deceased individuals.[43] He believed that he found evidence of a special structure at acupuncture points. However, several previous reports on the special structure of the needling points had already been discredited by the acupuncturists themselves after closer examination of the results. Furthermore, an anatomically fixed system cannot explain how points would shift in cases of disease and psychological stress, as another acupuncturist maintains.[44]

Even more difficult to prove than the variety of acupuncture points is a substantiation of the meridian system. The acupuncturists themselves admit that these meridians have nothing in common with nerves and blood vessels. The few explanations that have been published are based on extremely weak and shaky observations.[45,46]

What about medical research?

Some University Medical Centres in Europe and America have been using acupuncture to augment anaesthesia. In a paper on 500 operations at the German Heart Centre in Munich, Dr. Pongratz[47] reported a moderate decrease in the use of anaesthetic drugs. Patients remained conscious during complicated surgery and were able to communicate by nodding or shaking their heads.

Electro-acupuncture stimulation has also led to a decrease in post-operative complications.

In evaluating such reports it seems important to me to clarify the practice of acupuncture during anaesthesia in Western clinics. Anaesthesia is started as usual with a short period of general anaesthesia. During this time the needles are inserted and connected to a battery-powered control box. In addition, all the monitoring devices of modern medicine are installed. After about 30 minutes the patient is allowed to slowly and partially regain consciousness: he is more awake, but continues to be pain-free. Should he actually indicate pain, more analgesics are added to the intravenous infusion. In no case, however, is acupuncture used as the sole agent of anaesthesia.

Neurophysiologists (scientists exploring the functions of the nervous system) have established various theories which could explain the effects of electro-acupuncture as it is practised in Western operating theatres.

What they basically assume is taking place is *an unconscious distraction from pain* through acupuncture. Pain alleviation through distraction is not a new phenomenon - it was observed long before acupuncture appeared on the scene. War stories repeatedly tell about soldiers who, in the heat of a battle, lost an arm without feeling any pain. Only when the tension abated, did they start to feel the full impact of the excruciating pain in the grenade-torn stump.

Let us take a closer look at some of the scientific theories: first of all there is the *gate control theory*.[48] Canadian Psychology professor Dr. Melzack developed the hypothesis that a main impulse leads to a much weaker reaction in the brain, when the pressure receptors of the skin are simultaneously stimulated. This might explain why we rub our shin after hitting it against a corner: we actually follow the natural instinct to exert pressure on the skin to alleviate the pain-reaction in our brain. However, this hypothesis also has its weak points. Other researchers have contradicted and replaced it with new hypotheses. Certainly not all effects of acupuncture can be explained by it.[49]

A real sensation was created by research-findings in

mice, which demonstrated the excretion of a pain-reducing substance in the brain itself, after the mice had undergone needle stimulation.[50, 51] The substance, called *endorphin*, is similar to morphine, but is produced by the human body. Several of these endorphins have been isolated and their usefulness in medicine is being investigated. Further research has shown that endorphins are released when a patient swallows a fake-medication, called "placebo" in medical terminology, provided he firmly *believes* in its effectiveness.[52]

Scientists at the University of San Francisco studied some 50 patients who had to have a wisdom tooth removed. If you have ever had a tooth extracted you know something of the ferocious pain involved. It came as a surprise that in one test group satisfactory analgesia was reached even with completely ineffectual medications, provided that the patient *believed* in them. The main sensation returned after the injection of a drug which blocks the effect of endorphins in the brain.[53]

Thus there might well be some truth in the conclusions of those researchers who trace acupuncture back to *hypnosis* and *suggestion*.[54, 55] In two articles, Professor Wall, for example, describes his own experiences in China: the patients who were operated on under acupuncture-analgesia, displayed a rock-like faith in the method. They were taken into the hospital days or weeks before the operation and underwent intensive psychic training. The physicians spoke of the "spiritual aspects" of acupuncture to explain its effectiveness.

It is interesting to note that in China itself fewer and fewer patients are anaesthetised with the help of acupuncture. According to a report of the National Academy of Sciences in 1975, only about 10 per cent of all operations in China were performed with acupuncture-analgesia, and even then it was combined with Western methods of anaesthesia.[56] Even more disturbing is an article in the large Peking newspaper *Wenhui Bao*, where two Chinese doctors admitted that acupuncture had been used as a propaganda tool during the cultural revolution. Operations under purported acupuncture analgesia had been staged to impress foreigners. Many patients dared not scream although they did feel pain.[57]

Doubts have also been raised concerning the necessity to locate the exact points indicated on the acupuncture charts. Acupuncture stimuli are being given in such a chaotic way in China, writes Professor Wall, that it is impossible to start investigating the practice of acupuncture scientifically on this foundation. Research on volunteers in Toronto has shown that the needle-stimulation of wrong points led to the same-pain relieving effect.[58]

At a medical convention on anaesthesiology the co-worker of a renowned German acupuncture professor related to one of his colleagues, that needles had inadvertently fallen out during the operations on several patients. Nevertheless they did not feel pain because sufficient amounts of analgesics were being given in the drip.

While working for a year in the department of anaesthesiology at a large medical centre I have seen for myself, that low doses of analgesics may suffice in individual patients whilst an operation is being performed. It might well be that the publications of Dr. Pongratz[47] or Professor Herget[59] are not so much a proof of the effectiveness of acupuncture, but rather they might indicate that it takes less analgesic to produce freedom from pain than was assumed before.

The scientific "proofs" of acupuncture are so variable and contradictory, that the world-renowned American pain specialist, Dr. J.J. Bonica, will not use acupuncture for anaesthesia or for the cure of chronic ailments until there is more conclusive research available.[60]

I don't blame you if you are thoroughly confused. Isn't there anything to rely on? Until today acupuncture has remained a riddle that has escaped a scientific solution. There are models, as we have seen, but there are no conclusive answers.

The acupuncturists' failure to present scientific evidence has created *a lush culture medium for occult therapies*. Increasingly authors are not even bothering to explain acupuncture scientifically. They would rather rely on cosmic, spiritistic and occult powers, that are adorned with pseudoscientific labels. Dr. G. Fisch expresses a common notion, when he writes: "Acupuncture cannot be separated from Chinese medicine, the science of human energetics... We are far from a simple reflex-therapy to which acupuncture has been reduced in Europe through the ignorance of Chinese medicine."[61]

The perilous snake

According to the Hindus, a dangerous snake is lurking in every human being. Her name is *Kundalini* and she lies curled up at the end of the spine. Never attempt to wake her without the help of a Guru. If she raises her head and is released without control, she raves, and no man can resist her power.

For the Hindus the snake Kundalini symbolises the hidden supernatural energy slumbering in every man.[62] A special form of Yoga is designed to release her power, *Kundalini Yoga*. When the snake is awakened, she moves along fine channels, the Chakras, until she reaches the heart, where she takes up her new home.

But how does this myth relate to our topic? Various psychics have established a connection between Kundalini and the Chinese energy Ch'i. The channels followed by the snake correspond to the acupuncture meridians. Acupuncture, they say, is no different from a controlled manipulation of the snake Kundalini, as practised in Kundalini Yoga. Says Dr. Hiroshi Motoyama, director of the Institute for Religious Psychology in Tokyo: "The acupuncture points are the points where Western medicine, the Chinese medicine and Indian Yoga meet each other."[63]

Special efforts have been made to demonstrate that man is really permeated by cosmic energy. As early as 1854 a German, Freiherr von Reichenbach, had published a book, in which he described how "sensitive" persons emanated light in the darkness, an aura of a bluish, sometimes orange, glow.[64] In 1939 Soviet parapsychologist Kirlian discovered a photographic technique, named after him, which is supposed to show the energy field, or *aura*, around the human body.[65] If a person's hand is photographed between two plates of high voltage, the fingertips seem to radiate tiny bluish and reddish light effects. Serious scientists explain the phenomenon as an electrical one, caused by minute water droplets on the hand.[66] But undaunted, parapsychologists and acupuncturists all over the world are using Kirlian photographs to support their claims of the vital force postulated by Chinese and Hindu scriptures.[67]

Professor William Tiller at Stanford University believes that the material gathered so far is sufficient to prove that man not only has his physical body, but also an "astral body", as described in the Yoga literature, which says that the human body consists of seven levels. The first is the plane of the visible body. The second is called the etheric plane, and is said to be inhabited by an "etheric double" unable to leave the physical body. Its main task is thought to be the distribution of cosmic energy among the organs, thus maintaining health. This is the plane where acupuncture is supposed to have its effect. Further down the line, the third plane consists of the "astral body" roughly equivalent with the human soul and capable of leaving the body at the point of death to be reincarnated. Tiller adds further hypothetical planes which are not pertinent here.[68]

We could go on and on enumerating occult "proofs" for the existence of cosmic energies tapped by acupuncture. The more scientific research proves unable to render satisfactory explanations for the phenomenon of acupuncture, the more people are turning to the accounts of parapsychology regardless of whether they are true or not. The continuous stream of success stories ("miracle cures") in the media is convincing more and more people that Chinese/Hindu philosophies contain the underlying principles for the restoration of their health. As a consequence, people are increasingly opening their hearts to Eastern cults and turning their backs on God's truth as revealed in the Bible.

Death in the needle chaos

Acupuncture does not only present spiritual dangers but

medical complications as well. Most Western practitioners have acquired their art in a crash course of one to seven days. Nevertheless, their newly acquired weekend-skills are put into lucrative practice at rates ranging from £25-£100 per session.

Complications and failures are not infrequent but are rarely mentioned. An article in the Journal of the American Medical Association (JAMA) describes various severe complications after acupuncture treatment. The list includes infections at the needling sites, misdiagnoses, and even puncturing of the lungs.[69]

Especially tragic is the case of a physician who, while attending an introductory seminar on acupuncture, suffered a heart attack. Instead of rushing him to the hospital, the various "specialists" experimented with their needles on their unfortunate colleague. The ambulance crew who tried to resuscitate him were hindered at their actions as multiple small needles had to be removed from the patient's upper lip to enable a proper oxygen supply to be administered. When they finally succeeded in establishing an intravenous infusion, another naturopath tore the canula out, as he deemed that blood-letting was indicated. The final part in the "Death in the Needle Chaos", as a news magazine headline called it, was that the physician expired on his way to the hospital.[70]

This incident once more highlights that acupuncturists by far overestimate the list of ailments they claim to be able to cure.

Let me state very strongly: *no disease which is caused by a clearly organic change* (such as infections, nerve paralysis, cancer, hereditary ailments, arteriosclerosis, deafness, multiple sclerosis etc) *can be influenced by acupuncture*, in spite of the claims made by its proponents. This has been confirmed repeatedly in controlled studies.[36]

Undisputed, however, is the success in so-called *functional disorders*. These diseases are caused by a disturbance of an organ's function. For example, stress can lead to a change in the stomach's acid-production which can in turn lead to peptic ulcers developing. Similar factors seem to be involved in various skin diseases. The temporary relief of arthritic pain as well as that of migraines constitutes an area of amazing success for acupuncture. Again these pain conditions are greatly influenced by psychological factors.

But even the cure of functional diseases is not all that impressive when scrutinised more closely: controlled follow-up studies show that relief occurs only in about one third of the patients and lasts only for a short time. So many of the sufferers continue to search for healing.

Should a Christian submit to acupuncture therapy?

Having considered the background of acupuncture, let's deal with the crucial question: should a Christian who knows about these things submit to treatment by an acupuncturist?

To answer the question, let me draw a fine line between:

1. Acupuncture analgesia in a hospital setting.

2. Acupuncture for the proposed cure of diseases by medical doctors and Holistic Health practitioners.

Basically I am convinced that we cannot blame all the effects of acupuncture on demonic powers. Many of the successes acupuncturists claim are psychological and could have been brought about equally well by a fake medication (placebo) or with the help of a skilled psychologist. There are physicians who reject the occult-philosophical background of the acupuncture they practise. They are convinced that they are only influencing the autonomic nervous system (ANS) with their needles. These doctors are in the minority but we should be careful not to include them in the category of "demonic healers".

Most of them are to be found in general practice or in research labs and departments of anaesthesia in Western medical centres, although even there, occult models are sometimes used to explain acupuncture's effects. As we have seen, there are some theoretical explanations for the analgesic effects of acupuncture, but the additional use of drugs seems to have a major part in its purported success.

If you, as a Christian, cannot reconcile the use of acupuncture during anaesthesia with your conscience, simply tell the doctor in charge. "The method is not indicated," says German acupuncture professor Dr. Herget, "when patients have a negative attitude towards the procedure."[59]

Let us turn now to the second group, to those acupuncturists who want to *heal diseases* with their needles and who overwhelmingly rely on occult energies in their efforts to do so. I have asked several physicians and counsellors for their opinion on whether or not a Christian should undergo treatment from such therapists. Especially interesting is the view of a Christian doctor working among the Chinese, Dr. Peter Wee. Dr. Wee, who is Chinese himself, is in private practice in Singapore. He writes:

> Here in Singapore the acupuncturist is considered simply a practitioner of the art of Chinese medicine and nothing more. For the patient to seek help beyond what the acupuncturist can offer, he would go to a Buddhist temple and consult a medium. Perhaps the medium may resort to acupuncture depending on whether he has experience with it or not. Although acupuncture has been the rage in the West since President Nixon's visit to China in 1972, it has not affected medical practice here in Singapore at all. There are some Western-trained doctors who would like to "cash-in" on this craze, but by and large the public who frequent acupuncture clinics avoid Western-trained doctors, who may have taken a crash course in acupuncture. In the public mind, Western-trained doctors should stick to Western medicine, and leave acupuncture and herbal treatment to the practitioners of traditional (Chinese, Malay or other)

medicine.

There have been many instances of patients coming to see me after acupuncture-treatments (for arthritis, fibrositis, neuritis etc.) have failed. So far I have had no occasion to send any patient, much less a Christian patient, to an acupuncturist. The Western medicines which we exhibit are sufficient to meet the needs of most of the musculo-skeletal disorders that afflict mankind, and if the disease is incurable, an acupuncturist is in no better position to treat it, as many "treatments" are purely symptomatic. There have been claims of dramatic improvement with acupuncture, just as there have been claims of so-called miraculous healing in the charismatic movement.

Personally I have no experience with acupuncture, having never taken a course in it, nor having a desire to do so, as I have far too often seen the complications and misery which have arisen as the result of a patient's resorting to acupuncture. Hemiplegics, quadriplegics, paraplegics and cancer patients have spent vast sums of money on acupuncturists, all to no avail. In many instances the healing of musculo-skeletal disorders would have taken place even if Western drugs had been employed, or even if no medication has been given. We know too well how tissues heal themselves (in the wisdom of our Lord) without any intervention from drugs, herbs or needles.

Dr. Christian Klopfenstein, author of the book *La Bible et la Santé* (The Bible and Health), wrote to me:

Personally I believe that acupuncture is not a very accurate science. Even if some aspects have scientific explanations, nothing is very sure. Still there are some phenomena which could possibly be explained with scientific methods. However it seems obvious to me that the *spirit of magic and suggestion* have a strong influence on the results. All these unconventional methods demand the *faith* of the patient and if he will not put his faith in God and has no faith in medical science, then he puts it in alternatives. Man has a fundamental need to believe in something and to confide in somebody. If he does not believe in the true God, he puts his confidence into all sorts of deceit, counterfeits and things which lead him astray...

Battle for the mind

The battle for healing through acupuncture is taking place on a spiritual plane. It is *faith* in the practice that brings about the healing. "There are indications," says acupuncturist Schnorrenberger[71] regarding ear acupuncture, "that it is possible to induce mind changes by stimulating the ear, and to *manipulate man's soul*" (italics mine). And almost cultic sounds the promise of another acupuncturist: "People with whatever inner conflicts, I make them simply free."[72]

The question for Christians is: What is the goal? Is it really just relief from pain or does the acupuncturist aim at "harmony with cosmic energies"? The words of many acupuncturists and the promises of God are diametrically opposed to one another. If someone promises to "make you free" with the help of needles, he is offering you *stones for bread*. And if you submit to mind-change under acupuncture, your soul might well be manipulated - but by whom?

I have experienced personally what Mark Albracht of the San-Francisco based *Spiritual Counterfeits Project* wrote to me in a letter:

> While many types of psychic healing such as acupuncture, etc., may not be overtly anti-Christian or anti-Biblical, our experience indicates that people who pursue these areas for the most part end up adhering to some form of occult world view or Eastern-mystical practice.

Wrapping up our discussion, a paragraph from Dr. Duke's book on acupuncture might illustrate once more, how intricately the modern practice of acupuncture is interwoven with Eastern philosophy:

> The entire universe, he feels, works to such a precise orderly fashion, that it contains no mysteries beyond his scope of understanding. This is not arrogance, but a rich feeling of association between man and nature. Because no supreme power, no Lord of Hosts, created the world, the forces behind life and death and illness and health are not beyond man's comprehension. They are, in the form of Ch'i, present in every living creature, every tree and flower, every puff of wind and drop of rain.
>
> The acupuncturist sees the lives of his patients as integral parts of the universe. He brings his patients back to health not only for their own sake and happiness, but so that the whole world may function properly. *Every needle the acupuncturist twirls between his fingers bears the heavy weight of universal harmony in its slim, pointed end.*[73] (Italics mine).

The crucial questions Christians have to ask not only deal with the danger of occult oppression, but more importantly our basic attitude towards God and His Word. Who do we believe more, the Bible or the promises of Eastern philosophies? To what, or whom, are we surrendering our consciousness, to God or to esoteric powers that could manipulate our soul? This is where the real dangers of acupuncture lurk. Under the cloak of science and the claim to restore health, a subcutaneous dose of Eastern philosophy is surreptitiously injected into the patient. And it is with this in mind that Christians must decide whether they want to use or recommend the method or not.

As the apostle Paul exhorts us:

> See to it that no one takes you captive through hollow and deceptive philosophy, which depends on human tradition and the basic principles of this world rather than on Christ. For in Christ all the fullness of the Deity lives in bodily form, and you have been given fullness in Christ, who is the head over every power and authority.[74]

Five

Reflexology - "Laying Hands" on the Feet

Whenever 53 year old machinist John Perry [a] feels the muscles of his neck getting tight, he knows that he will soon have one of his migraine attacks. He leaves his work for a few minutes, and goes down to the changing rooms in the basement. He sits on a bench, takes off his shoes and socks, bends his knee and starts to slowly massage his big toe. After a few minutes he changes position and repeats the same ritual on the other foot. Then he returns to his machine.

Jim Perry is practising a new healing method for his minor ailment which is attracting more and more people. He trusts in reflexology.

As ancient as acupuncture

What is reflexology? What is its origin? The history of the therapy takes us all the way back to the era of ancient Chinese and Indian traditional medicine.[1] It has the same roots as acupuncture. The ancient practitioners not only used needles but also treated their patients by massaging different pressure-points. Similar techniques were also found in the traditional medicine of American Indians.[2]

It is not surprising to find in the philosophical background of reflexology all the elements of Eastern philosophy we have already encountered in acupuncture. Let us review them for a moment and compare them with the writings of foot reflexologists.

(a) Names and circumstances have been changed throughout the book to protect the privacy of individuals

1. *Macrocosm and Microcosm Correlate with and Influence One Another*

In an article Mrs Hanne Marquardt, author of a major textbook on reflexology, mentions iridology, ear acupuncture and palmistry and further writes:

> In the same way that you hear the common notion of our time that the particular is a reflection of the whole. . . we are also confronted with this knowledge in the particularities of our feet .[3]

Also in her book she says:

> The overall condition of our body is reflected in our feet like a little monitor. . . Every organ has its corresponding reflex zone on a part of the foot, from which a body zone leads to that organ.[4]

2. *Man Lives in a Cosmic Energy Field and is Constantly Permeated by Energy*

Reflexologist Davaki Berkson writes:

> The feet are one of the most effective body areas on which to practise reflexology because they are strong energy poles of the body and they link with the energy emanations from the earth, especially from the grass, sand and snow.[5]

The author, who thanks Christ, Swami Satchinananda and Yogi Bhajan for guiding her on this path, continues:

> The art of healing through the Integrated Treatment recognises the universal healing forces that are present throughout the universe at all times.[6]

3. *Disease is the Consequence of an Energy Imbalance*

Here is another quote from a reflexologist:

> It is the task of the therapist to search for points in the patient's body which are imbalanced and reflected in the microsystem of the foot. Our great helper is the sensation of pain. From acupuncture we know that "Pain is the tissue's scream of flooding energy."[7]

4 Treatment is accomplished by the Channelling of Energy according to the Principles of Yin and Yang

> Good health is a matter of balance. From the organs to the reflex points there are pathways, or currents, through which pass the all-important energies our bodies need to maintain balance and vibrance. These energy currents can be mapped on the body in the same way as highways are marked on a map. Reflexology removes the blocks that impede the proper flow of the body's energy currents. The methodology is simple, much like learning to push the right button (reflex points) on a computer (the body) to balance the energy of the body and allow good health to permeate the entire system.[8]

The idea of Yin and Yang is also alluded to:

> We are working on the reflex zones with a special technique, a wavelike movement, subordinated in its polarity (activity and relaxation) to pivotal principles of life. All life is characterised by this polarity: take e.g. the opposites of winter and summer, flood and tide or inspiration and expiration. . .[9]

These few selected quotations demonstrate that foot reflexology belongs to the group of natural healing methods which have their basis in Eastern philosophy.

Human anatomy condensed in the feet

These ancient Chinese principles were rediscovered by American ear, nose and throat specialist Dr. William Fitzgerald. Together with another physician, he published a book, *Zone Therapy*, describing patient histories and therapeutic plans for family doctors, dentists, gynaecologists, ear, nose and throat specialists and chiropractors.[10]

He divided the human body into 10 perpendicular "reflex zones", representing all organs of the body. "Impurities of the blood" are supposed to descend along these lines, finally settling as crystalline urea in the nerve endings of the soles of the feet, where experienced reflexologists claim to be able to feel them. These deposits would then not only indicate which organ was affected but would also be important to treatment as massaging the spots[11] would dissolve the impurities.

Basically Fitzgerald did nothing more than take the drawings of his anatomical textbook and project them on soles of the feet as accurately as possible. The brain found its representation in the big toe, the heart on the left and the kidneys in the arch of the foot. When he could not fit all the organs on the soles, he expanded his system to include both sides of the feet up to the ankles. Thus it became, supposedly, possible to treat all the organs from the brain to the hip, from the wisdom teeth to the small intestine, by massaging the feet.

This new miracle therapy soon spread all over America and in 1923 "was more popular than any other manual therapy described in medical journals".[12] Dr. Fitzgerald and his followers even performed minor operations on the ear, nose and throat while the only anaesthesia - faithful to the model of acupuncture - was produced by an assistant who massaged the patient's feet.[13] However, like all vogues, reflexology was soon forgotten in America and only the nostalgia brought on by the Seventies brought this relic of days gone by back to the surface. The American Medical Association calls reflexology simply "a cult".[14]

Reflex zones - but not in the feet

Although serious practitioners of reflexology admit that the effects and claims of their art cannot be proved scientifically, other adherents have repeatedly attempted to explain reflexology with traditional models of science.

The term "reflex zone" was not originally coined by Dr. Fitzgerald but by Dr. Head who published his discovery of reflectory zones in the human body, especially the trunk, as early as 1898.[15] Quite unlike the foot reflex zones, these reflex areas can be explained medically, as in cases of gall bladder (biliary) colic. Although the disorder is primarily in the gall bladder or internal organs, external muscles are also affected because they are connected by fine nerve-fibres. The muscles become stiff and painful, and one dares not move because of the excruciating pain. Warm poultices applied to these places can bring about miraculous relief.

We have to emphasise, however, that Head's reflex zones only exist on the trunk, where the body consists of well-defined segments of skin, muscles and nerves which have a definite relation with the internal organs. They are positively not applicable to foot reflexology.

It seems that there are further reflex zones in the soft tissues of the trunk. Many applications of physiotherapy in the hospital setting are based on soft tissue massage.[16] Professional massage of these areas and the application of warm packs may lead to marked improvement in functional and chronic diseases.[17]

The effects of massage, however, are not facilitated through reflexes as was previously assumed. New research has demonstrated that a physiotherapist's strokes release substances to the skin which influence the blood vessels. Thus massage may lead to effects in organs far removed from the actual rubbing site, leading to improved circulation.[18]

It is a well-documented fact that all these forms of

massage also have a psychological component. This is readily admitted by one of the foremost specialists in physiotherapy Prof. Dr. A. Kohlrausch:

> The fact alone that they are regularly treated over a prolonged period of time, is of great significance to many patients. The therapist's active attention gives the patient the comforting feeling that something is being done for him. As the therapy has to be applied individually, it undoubtedly has positive aspects, due to the eminently important contact between patient and therapist achieved through the "laying on of hands."[19]

Therefore, psychological factors probably play an important part in the success of reflexologists and healers. Those who stubbornly insist on the reality of reflexes have to accept the criticism of Dr. Uexkuell, Professor of Psychosomatics. In discussing Pavlov who originally introduced the concept of reflexes, Dr. Uexkuell states that this teaching led to a situation "where one was not allowed to talk about the soul anymore except in terms of reflexes."[20]

Often during a massage a conversation will develop between therapist and patient, something that he often misses most in the doctor's surgery. Mrs Marquardt writes: "The range of elicited emotions is wide ranging from uncontrollable crying to the open discussion of problems".[21]

There are certainly reflex zone therapists who want to have nothing to do with its philosophical background, or the frequently involved occult practices. Among them are sincere Christians who even try to provide counselling during their therapy if the opportunity arises. I do not believe that their treatment leads to occult oppression.

Nonetheless they cannot be spared the reproach of indirectly promoting a philosophy which has its origin in Eastern mysticism and has already led many away from the gospel. Moreover, the medical value of reflexology is very limited, even when the therapist is a Christian.

Cosmic energy through laying hands on the feet

When I started to do my research I wanted to take a course in reflexology myself. I wrote to two institutions that advertised their training seminars in a New Age magazine. Can you imagine my surprise when I opened the first letter. The institute not only offered me a course in reflexology but also in the use of the radionic pendulum! I knew about the occult implications of this technique and waited for the prospectus from the other institute. This time I got a letter from a lady who not only massages her patients' feet but also reads their future from their palms.

Shortly afterwards I read the testimony of a young American who had come out of a cult. He reported that they had been practising "Castaneda sorcery; performing Yoga exercises, meditating, chanting and doing foot massage; being hypnotised; taking drugs and having trips".[22]

Slowly it dawned on me that this new therapy which was so enthusiastically praised was frequently being practised by healers who were involved in the occult.

A lady who had previously been taking up to ten pills a day had turned to reflexology. In her missionary zeal for this new way of salvation she sent me the book *Health for the Future*.[23] Besides fully coloured diagrams of the reflex zones of the feet, the book also gave advice for a healthier life style. But in the same way that medieval cooks mixed poison into a superb meal to get rid of an unpleasant person, the book included a chapter about dangerous energy emanations along with some otherwise good information. It then explained to the patient that detrimental "water veins" were responsible for the morning blues and for headaches and joint pains which disappear shortly after getting up. More disturbingly, it said that these water veins were supposed to cause cancer.

"Unfortunately these radiations have not yet been demonstrated scientifically", regrets the author. However she gives advice on how to engage a dowser to find the cancer-causing "cold spots". To protect oneself against the detrimental effects of the radiation she recommends putting a little plastic tub with a mirror in it under the bed, a method "which will be as effective after ten years as on the first day".

Christians should realise that these practices belong to the category of superstition and occultism (see Chapter 8). How can we submit, with a clear conscience, to healers who practise these things?

The ancient Chinese massage therapists had a higher goal in their treatment than just rubbing away detrimental deposits of urea crystals:

> Practitioners have described their conscious mental state as devoid of conceptual thought. This allows them to concentrate and channel their Ki strongly and evenly during treatment. By acting in this state of awareness, the practitioner believes that his treatment may relate with the natural process of life rhythms that will flow more evenly and strongly through him to his patients.[24]

"Actually I had seen the pendulum hanging in the waiting room," Mrs Black, a Bible-believing Christian, told me. "But I thought: when he rubs my feet he won't use the pendulum, will he? When he rubbed the headache zone on my big toe, I suddenly saw this absent-minded expression on his face, as if he were in a trance. I asked him, 'What are you doing?' He replied: 'I am concentrating in order to channel vital energy into your body.' The next day, when I tried to have my quiet time as usual, I felt no more joy in Bible-reading and prayer. I realised what I had dabbled in, and asked Jesus Christ to forgive me."

Mrs. Black regained her spiritual freedom. But her example demonstrates that many reflexologists seem to use powers in their therapy which do not originate in God.

The experience of counsellors has shown repeatedly that

physical contact can be a bridge for demonic powers to enter another person.[25] Spiritistic books recommend holding hands during a seance in order for every participant to experience the energy of the spirit.[26] The dangers of uncritical submission to the laying on of hands should not be underestimated, even if it happens in a religious setting.

It should no longer be a taboo to question a reflexologist's world view. Is he really just trying to dissolve purportedly pathogenic substances and to bring about muscular relaxation? Or is his work based on the idea of harmonising cosmic energies in the patient? In view of the limited therapeutic value of reflexology, Christians should seriously consider whether a method with a background of such New Age philosophy really can be the solution for their problems.

Six

Homoeopathy - Cosmic Energy in Bottles

When you ask people about homoeopathy, you will get all sorts of answers. For example: "Isn't that natural medicine without side effects?" or "Doesn't the Queen have a Royal homoeopathic doctor among her physicians?" But nobody is quite sure what homoeopathy is. Already very popular in Europe and Great Britain, homoeopathy is now having a renaissance in the US under the auspices of the Holistic Health movement.

What is homoeopathy?

The basic definition was given by its founder Samuel Hahnemann (1755 - 1843): "Similia similibus curantur" or "like is healed by like". Another homoeopath gave this definition:

> Homoeopathy gives the patient a remedy
> that will cause the same symptoms in a
> healthy person as those that are observed
> in the one who is sick.

Let's take a simple practical example: somebody suffers from diarrhoea. We all know that castor oil causes diarrhoea in a healthy individual, therefore, according to homoeopathy principles you have to treat the patient with castor oil. If the poor patient, however, had the castor oil in its usual concentration, he would probably get stuck in the lavatory forever. This is why the remedy has to be diluted. Which brings us to an important element of homoeopathy: the *principle of dilution*.

Superficially considered, homoeopaths try to use the

smallest possible amount of a drug. Dilutions are marked with an "X", showing how often the original tincture was diluted, usually by factors of ten. A dilution of "12 X", commonly used by many homoeopaths, is therefore the mixture of 1 cubic-centimetre of original tincture with 100,000,000,000 cubic centimetres of solvent (water or alcohol). In other words, one teaspoon of active substance is added to a tank the size of the Empire State Building in New York. Many homoeopaths go even further. Hahnemann preferred a dilution of "30 X"; a concentration that would not even allow one single molecule of the original substance in a bottle,

To explain the reason why the remedy is nonetheless supposed to work, we must take a look at another basic assumption of homoeopathy, *potentiation*. It will lead us right into the conceptual world of cosmic forces and Eastern philosophy.

When a homoeopathic pharmacist prepares a remedy, he first needs a mother tincture, for example by extracting the active ingredients of minced herbs with alcohol. Then he takes one drop of the mother tincture, mixes it with 9 drops of alcohol and rapidly shakes it in a vial. He now has a dilution of one tenth or what is called "potency 1" (1 X). Then one part of this mixture is added to nine parts of the neutral base and shaken again, thus yielding potency 2, and so on.

Wouldn't it be easier to mix one drop of the mother tincture with the equivalent of 999,999 drops to get to the 6th potency? Why is the remedy prepared in steps of 1:10 dilutions? Hahnemann was convinced:

> ...that there is more to the process of succession than simple dilution. Shaking (or potentiating) releases dynamic energies. What dark Mesmer conveys directly, Hahnemann facilitates indirectly: via the living human hand he is 'laying hands' on the sick.[1]

In other words, Hahnemann believes that through

shaking his remedies, a cosmic *vital force*[2] is transferred to the homoeopathic solution. The power that is transmitted directly in psychic healing through the laying on of the healer's hand, is now thought to be carried by the homoeopathic medicine and conveyed indirectly.

Who was Samuel Hahnemann?

To understand a movement, it helps to take a closer look at its founder's life. The story of Samuel Hahnemann illustrates particularly the fact that justified rebellion against grievances of one's time cannot lead to a solution for the world's problems, if carried out in an anti-Christian spirit.

Hahnemann's life has been described at length in various biographies.[3, 4, 5] Let me give only a few highlights: he was born in Meissen, Saxonia, in 1755, as the son of a porcelain painter. Being a highly gifted student he was able to study medicine in Leipzig, Vienna and Erlangen. Several attempts to settle in private practice failed, and most of the time he and his family of nine children lived in extreme poverty. In his restlessness they moved from one town to another more than twenty times. Hahnemann earned his living by translating books from French, Italian and English into German. Besides that, he was constantly tinkering with new drugs. He became increasingly known as a caustic critic of medicine as it was practised during his time. After the death of his first wife, he married a second time when he was 80. A famous and wealthy physician at last, he died in Paris in 1843.

With regard to the medical situation in the 18th century, it is no wonder that Hahnemann rebelled against it. Bloodletting was considered a universal treatment. One therapy for pneumonia prescribed the letting of seven quarts of blood within a fortnight. Most of the time the patient was "healed" by his death. Other doctors prescribed opium by the pound or tried to purge the body with the help of daily enemas or red-hot irons.

Hahnemann realised intuitively that most of the medical practices of those days could not offer any real help. In essays and books he became more and more caustic in his criticism, denouncing his colleagues as "health-destructive egg heads."[6] One is immediately reminded of modern-day critics of medicine, such as Norman Shealy, M.D. (*Occult Medicine Can Save your Life*),[7] or Dr. Robert Mendelsohn (*Confessions of a Medical Heretic*)[8] who are waging war against overly technical medicine in a similarly raucous manner. They are expressing that dull gut-level feeling that something must be wrong with a medicine which is not treating man as a "whole".

Over the years Hahnemann's character changed in a strange way. He became increasingly gruff, impatient and undependable. He broke off relations with friends of many years, and even those people who supported him, had to endure his abrupt and unrestrained tantrums.[9] His gradual personality change began increasingly to affect his children. Their lives were a series of tragedies: the marriages of three daughters ended in divorce, two daughters were murdered in a mysterious way, and another daughter died when she was 30. His only son, Friedrich, deserted his wife and child, never to come back.[10] One of his biographers says, "Friedrich Hahnemann had to empty the cup of demonism with which his father had endowed him."[11]

In the year 1810, Hahnemann published his major work, the *Organon of Medicine*. It was preceded by studious research over many years. He developed the idea of homoeopathy when he translated a book by English physician W. Cullen, describing the effects of quinine (Peruvian bark) on malaria. Hahnemann tried the drug himself, and found that it caused symptoms similar to malaria: fever, chills and general malaise.*

---

* These symptoms could never be verified in later experiments with healthy test persons. Hahnemann had taken quinine earlier in his life, and it is quite probable that his experiment had caused an *allergic reaction*, which can typically occur with the symptoms Hahnemann described.[13] However, he interpreted them as malaria symptoms. Thus, homoeopathy, similar to iridology, is based on the *error of its discoverer*.

The attacks would last for two to three hours, beginning soon after he had ingested the drug; apart from that he was fine.[12] All of a sudden Hahnemann was enlightened: the same substance that caused fever in a healthy person, healed the fever of a patient. Now he started to experiment with innumerable substances, "proving" their effects on himself, his family and his friends. Every symptom, insignificant though it seemed, was painstakingly registered. 1,422 "proving symptoms" were supposedly found with Belladonna (the extract of the deadly nightshade), 1,267 with Nux vomica (vomit nut), and 1,163 with the flower Pulsatilla.[14]

More than that Hahnemann constructed a relationship between the "character of a remedy" and the "homoeopathic character" of a patient.[15] It would take too long to explain all the ramifications of the homoeopathic doctrine of characterology, but if you are looking for an extensive description you will find it in James Tyler Kent's *Repertory of the Homoeopathic Materia Medica*.[16]

The most difficult problem Hahnemann (and modern physicians) faced was that of chronic diseases. Why was it that so many people did not experience healing with his medicines? He attempted an answer in the work of his late years, *The Chronic Diseases, Their Peculiar Nature and Homoeopathic Healing*. There he proposed that seven out of eight cases of chronic diseases were caused by "psora" or the "inner miasm."[17] Should the medication hit one of its tentacles, innumerable new ones would immediately spring up. The disease would react with "particular ferocity" when it was deprived of its external expression of the deep-rooted evil, the skin eruption. Here is his advice for all chronically ill: take one single dose of homoeopathic sulfur every 30 to 50 days.

Even his devout biographer Gumpert who compares him to Goethe, Kant and Martin Luther, is puzzled: "This way of practising homoeopathy is a *unique psychic phenomenon, demanding an almost Indian ability to meditate and concentrate far beyond our limits of experience.*"(Italics mine)

And he is right: an examination of the underlying philosophy of homoeopathy shows its relationship to

Eastern ideology.

Several terms which are repeated time and again in homoeopathic books make one stop and think. They talk of the *vital force, harmony with the universe,* the *ethereal body.* All these expressions sound very similar to the teachings which have been brought to the West by Gurus and Yogis. The more you get into the writings of Hahnemann and his disciples, the more you have to realise that homoeopathy is intertwined in Eastern philosophy.

As a young man Hahnemann had become a member of the *Freemasons.*[18] This movement uses a lot of Christian sounding words and there is even a Bible on the altars of most Masonic temples. However, the Freemasons clearly deny the message of the Gospel, thus rejecting the salvation of lost men through Christ's sacrifice on the cross.[19] To them salvation lies in man himself. Says one author:[20] "Freemasonry teaches that all good men, whatever their personal beliefs, have a right to hope for salvation. Each mason can for himself work out his own conception of God, and thereby achieve salvation." Counselling practice has shown that Freemasons who really turn to Jesus Christ immediately become aware of the necessity to leave the lodge.[21]

It is no surprise that Hahnemann, as a member of the lodge, disparagingly *called Jesus an "arch-enthusiast."*[22] One of his biographers writes:

> He took offence at the arch-enthusiast Jesus of Nazareth, who did not lead the enlightened on the straight way to wisdom but who wanted to struggle with publicans and sinners on a difficult path towards the establishment of the kingdom of God. . . . the man of sorrows who took the darkness of the world on Himself was an offence to the lover of etheric wisdom.[23]

He further says:

> Hahnemann certainly was not a Christian

> although he is bigoted like a pietist.
> Hahnemann's god is consistently
> intervening with his guiding and giving
> power, but he is giving enlightenment to
> the mind, not touching the heart . . . .At the
> bedside of the sick, Hahnemann is a
> physician, and he cannot help it. But in his
> struggles as a spiritual seeker, in his plight
> for enlightenment, he is *strongly attracted
> to the East. Confucius is his ideal*.[24] (italics
> mine)

On Confucius, Hahnemann himself writes in a letter:

> This is where you can read divine wisdom,
> without miracle-myths and superstition. I
> regard it as an important sign of our times
> that Confucius is now available for us to
> read. Soon I will embrace him in the
> kingdom of blissful spirits, the benefactor
> of humanity, who has shown us the
> straight path to wisdom and to God,
> already 650 years before the arch-
> enthusiast.[25]

Is it possible to describe more clearly the spirit which has developed homoeopathy? The reverence for Eastern thought was not just Hahnemann's personal hobby, but rather the fundamental philosophy behind the preparation of homoeopathic remedies.

One of the foremost homoeopaths in Switzerland is Adolf Voegeli. I met the famous author of many books and polemic pamphlets on homoeopathy in a Zurich hotel and we talked about the way homoeopathy works. Smoking his self-made cigarettes, he told me about his experiences with homoeopathy; how he had cured mountain valley farmers of pneumonia exclusively with homoeopathic remedies and how he had treated managers in Lausanne when they presented with duodenal ulcers. When I asked him about the cosmic energy which was supposedly working through homoeopathy, he explained: "You know, I believe in the power of the zodiac. An astrologer predicted seven years in advance who my second wife would be, before I even knew her."

Dr. Voegeli has written an article on the mechanisms of homoeopathy which was published in the *Zeitschrift fuer Klassiche Homoeopathie* (Journal for Classical Homoeopathy).[26] The bibliography resembles a collection of occult, hinduistic and anthroposophical literature. Voegeli underscores that the effect of high potencies in homoeopathy is of a *"spiritual nature"*. His best explanation is supplied by the *hinduistic Sankhya philosophy*. According to it man not only has his physical body but also an *ethereal body* with a special system of energetic channels. It is this ethereal body that co-ordinates the immunological functions and enhances the wound-healing process. And it is here that homoeopathy is active.

Another energy system, he continues, is the *astral body* controlling the emotional responses of man. But the highest energy plane is the human spirit. Its purpose is to develop into an ever more perfect instrument for divine cosmic impulses. "The goal of man is a continuous evolution; his spiritualization." As one life is never enough, he logically brings in *reincarnation*, which would finally lead to perfection.

Eastern philosophy seeps through the writings of many other authors. George Vithoulkas, in his book *Homoeopathy - Medicine of the New Man*, writes in the same vein: "A disease is not just the malfunction of some organ but, first of all, a disturbance of the vital force that is responsible for the functioning of the whole organism."[27] Similarly, British homoeopath, Dr. J.P. Randeira, states that "homoeopathic medicines, through the process of potentiation, are able to restore the harmonic flow of the vital forces in every single human cell."[28] Another homoeopath expresses this principle with an almost religious ardour: "Under the holy act of potentiation, healing energy is released from the shackles of earthly structure to regenerate harmony in the ailing organism."[29]

How closely the homoeopathic concept of healing and

cosmic harmony is related to the Eastern concept of
salvation is revealed in the title of a book on homoeopathy
called *The Zodiac and the Salts of Salvation*.[30] This book
describes the importance of astrology in homoeopathy.
Thus, if you work through the underbrush of homoeopathic
language, you will find the golden thread of Eastern
philosophy throughout the modern practice of
homoeopathy.

Homoeopathy today

Having read through the odd ideas of Hahnemann, it is
difficult to believe that there are still people in the age of
science who would fully support this Guru of
homoeopathy. The contrary is true. In Germany alone more
than 1000 doctors and 3500 officially accredited health
practitioners practise homoeopathy. Homoeopathic
medicine enjoys widespread acceptance in France, Britain,
India and South America, and is regaining popularity in the
United States. The philosophical and medical conceptions
of today's homoeopaths may sound new, but they basically
remain faithful to the teachings of Hahnemann.

We have to distinguish between *three types of
homoeopaths*:

1. Those who have "demythologised" homoeopathy and
neither prescribe extremely diluted, nor "cosmically
energised" remedies. In most cases they do not exceed the
potency of 6X - 12X to make sure that an organic effect
would still be possible. They don't care about the
philosophical backgrounds and do not "potentiate" their
remedies after Hahnemann's model. What they want is a
natural remedy without detrimental side effects.

2. The second group is embarrassed by the medical
theories of Hahnemann which have been proven wrong.
Various researchers are trying, with the help of the latest
scientific technologies, to bring about new support for
homoeopathy.[54] Their efforts are marred, however, by the
fact that one of the research tools is the radionic pendulum[31]

which makes the results rather questionable.

3. The third group blindly believes in Hahnemann's teachings. His theories on the "miasm" as the cause of chronic diseases are not taken literally any more, but are understood and accepted as esoteric truths. These people openly admit their faith in astrology and other occult practices. A particularly active group in this category are the "Anthroposophes"[32, 33] as well as many adherents of "classical homoeopathy".

"Strophantus gratus" cures fear of pointed objects

Let me pick out a few examples from the multitude of homoeopathic teachings to illustrate the current state of affairs in homoeopathy. All examples are taken from recently published books. The first quotation from a book by F. Gauss entitled *How to Find the Proper Remedy* illustrates blind faith in Hahnemann's theories.[34] Like Hahnemann, Gauss makes the most subtle differentiations in his diagnoses. Thus he lists not fewer that 24 forms of fear - every form requiring a different medication. Anxiety before giving birth to a child is treated with "Cimicifuga" (Black cohosh) in a potentiation of 30X, "fear that something might come out of a corner" with Phosphor 6X, "fear of being touched, combined with severe sadness and a miserable mood" requires "Antimonium crudum" and "fear of pointed objects (knives, forks and the like)" is treated with "Strophantus gratus", 6X, the extract being made from an African plant containing heart-active substances.

In his republished *Lectures on Homoeopathic Philosophy*,[35] homoeopath Dr. James Tyler Kent describes the indications of "Nux vomica" (vomit nut):

> If it be a *Nux vomica* patient who has a prolapsed uterus, what would she say of herself that would make you see *Nux* in it? She would be chilly; full of choryza, with a stuffed up nose when in a warm room; she would be very iritable, snappy and would

want to kill her husband. She would probably be constipated and every uterine pain she had would would make her want to defaecate; straining to do so and only passing a small motion, one would want to go more frequently. You see at once that she has the generals of *Nux*, and whatever particulars she has are in harmony with those generals, and so you go from generals to particulars.
(p.211).

As you can imagine, this bizarre way of arriving at a diagnosis makes communication with modern Western medicine very difficult. More than that: what do a uterine prolapse and a stuffed up nose have in common? On what basis does Gauss arrive at his decision to prescribe "Strophantus gratus" in the concentration 6X and nothing else in no other concentration for "fear of pointed objects"? But these questions only touch the surface of what it is all about.

Where is the energy from?

The next example on the state of modern homoeopathy is taken from Paul Uccusic's book *Naturheiler* (Natural Healers).[36] He reports on "scientific" research at the Ludwig Boltzmann Institute in Vienna, whose director, Dr. Bischko, has written one of the most important text books for Western acupuncturists. It is at this Institute that a certain Dr. Otto Maresch investigates the healing powers of high potencies (30X to 1000X and more). We have seen that such a dilution would not leave one molecule in a single bottle. The healing power, say the homoeopaths, is coming from *cosmic power* transferred to the remedy through the ritual of potentiation.

As it is not possible to measure this cosmic vital energy with the help of scientific instruments, Dr. Maresch uses other means. Uccusic writes: "One should not take offence in the fact that Maresch uses bio-indicators to demonstrate the radiation of microwaves, namely a dowsing rod and pendulum". After being assured that the psycho-divination tools, the rod and pendulum, are only neutral scientific "bio-indicators", the reader is then acquainted with the concept of microwaves. In the same way that a microwave oven emits invisible radiation in order to cook a meal in a few minutes, a human being, an organ, a cancerous tumor or a drug emits their special vibrations. Whereas everyone knows that a microwave oven needs energy, Uccusic never gives a clue as to where the energy in homoeopathic remedies comes from.

According to Maresch "a homoeopathic remedy will have a better effect if its primary frequency corresponds to that of the vibrations of the affected organ or the sick system."To find a specific remedy for every disease in a given individual patient he has designed the following experiment. The test person is connected to a *biofeedback* system in order to tap his or her *meridians or acupuncture points*. To search for a remedy against cancer, the test person touches a little container which holds the pulverised form of a genuine tumour. The needle on the instrument jumps to the maximum. Now certain remedies are brought into the vicinity of the tumour to test their ability to neutralise the "cancerous vibrations". After several unsuccessful attempts, suddenly the needle falls back to zero. The surprising result: violet-tincture in the homoeopathic potency 8X to 12X is effective against cancer!

But there is a simpler method. "It is easier to take a shortcut with the radionic pendulum" and detect this "scientific" radiation. Even with the "neutral" electromagnetic instrument, something more is necessary and not every doctor can learn it, because it requires a certain sensitivity. Sensitivity to what? Why are these vibrations only picked up by certain sensitive persons? What energies are measured? Dr. Kurt Koch uses, instead of the term "sensitivity", the word "psychic powers". He writes:

> Psychic powers are mostly found in the
> relatives of those who have practised

> sorcery. If the forefathers up to the third or
> even fourth generation were spiritists or if
> they practised magic and other forms of
> occult activity, the descendants are usually
> psychic . . . Sensitivity to the rod and
> ability to make a pendulum react are
> psychic powers.[37]

Scientific research into homoeopathy

The results of scientific research into homoeopathy are
very controversial among experts in the field. Many
homoeopaths still maintain that homoeopathic effects
cannot be investigated by scientific methods.[38] Some
however, have done serious large-scale studies,[55] albeit
clearly limiting their relevance with the words that they do
"not allow comment on everyday clinical practice."[56]

Thus, along with many other physicians, I am personally
not convinced that homoeopathy can be proved by
scientific methods. I have been confirmed in this attitude by
an extremely interesting book on the subject, entitled
Homoeopathy and Science.[39] Unfortunately, it is not possible,
within the limits of this book, to give a detailed account of
the authors' findings. Most interesting is a report by Dr.
Donner, M.D., a homoeopath himself, who made the
scientific proof of homoeopathy his goal.[40]

However, the first serious attempt of a homoeopath to
find the truth in the jungle of homoeopathic claims ended in
a fiasco with Dr. Donner turning away from his pseudo-
religious faith in homoeopathy.

Dr. Donner's doubts had been aroused in a lecture at the
homoeopathic Robert Bosch Hospital in Stuttgart, Germany.
A well known homoeopath explained to his audience that
the remedy "Apis mellifica" was most effective in patients
with diseases on the right side, in connection with "lack of
thirst" and "a swelling under the right eye". He further
claimed that it was very effective in the treatment of right
sided ovarian cysts, whereas cysts on the left side required
a different medicine.

When Dr. Donner started reading through older reports

on the effects of "Apis mellifica" (which is nothing other than bee poison), he found not only that it had been used for twice as many diseases on the left side, but that the "swelling under the eye" had been caused by the application of the bee-poison.

His doubts could not be suppressed any more, and over the years he conducted experiments with almost two hundred doctors,.testing potencies 4X to 12X. He compared the "effective" homoeopathic remedies with completely neutral substances which are called "placebos" in medicine.

The results were startling. The first tests with the ineffective placebos caused numerous symptoms in those test subjects who believed in homoeopathy, in some cases so fiercely that the test had to be discontinued. After having taken placebos for three days, a participating doctor got such fierce attacks of migraine that she could only work part-time for half a year. The "unbelievers", on the other hand, did not register any symptoms, neither with the placebos nor with the homoeopathic remedies.

Particularly revealing was the behaviour of a homoeopathic doctor on the supervising board of the tests. In one experiment with "Nux vomica" in the astronomical potency of 60% he forgot that placebos had been given first. He looked at the test reports and started selecting those symptoms he anticipated with "Nux vomica"! Symptoms that did not fit, were simply omitted. This incident showed another weak point in the long lists of "proving symptoms" that were compiled in the history of homoeopathy: when the test supervisor knows what remedy is given, he only takes those symptoms he regards as significant and drops the rest.

This has nothing in common with the honest search for truth which should be so important to Christians. Nevertheless, I do not believe that most homoeopaths are consciously lying. However, their thinking runs so deep in the ruts of homoeopathic reasoning that they are no longer capable of critically evaluating some disturbing facts.

More minerals in vegetables than in homoeopathy

If weakness and disease really depended on the lack of certain trace elements and mineral salts alone, there would be no reason to take homoeopathic remedies or "biochemical" salts. "Despite all cleaning and cooking efforts in modern kitchens, our daily food contains more 'Calcarea', 'Silicea', 'Carbonicum' and other substances commonly used in homoeopathy than the remedies traded with these labels."[41] Why take all those homoeopathic remedies when their substances are already abundant in our natural surroundings?

A favourite argument to support homoeopathic theories is the analogy with immunisation. Isn't this an accepted method - to heal like with like? Subcutaneous injections of dead or weakened viruses are able to prevent exactly those diseases which are caused by the viruses. Although this is true in some cases, homoeopaths do not say that this preventive measure only applies to a very few of the more than 10,000 known diseases. Neither do they attempt to demonstrate that homoeopathic remedies activate the same immune mechanisms that are stimulated by a vaccination. It would be futile to try to compare the two, as these mechanisms do not apply to homoeopathy.

This example, shows, however, how scientific discoveries are taken out of context to support bizarre claims. Chief-coroner in Germany's capital, Bonn, Prof. Dr. Prokop, acknowledges the "brilliant ability" of homoeopaths "to identify scientific data with homoeopathic foundations - reasoning that is irrational ."[42]

Why is homoeopathy so successful?

There is no doubt that homoeopathy is successful. Everyone among my readers will have probably heard reports of how friends and relatives were wonderfully cured through a homoeopathic remedy prescribed by a health practitioner or physician. I do not want to discard these reports entirely, but the question is: What was it that actually healed them? The remedy? The cosmic occult vital force in the remedy? The accompanying measures (no smoking, no alcohol, taking a holiday)? Or faith in the healer or his remedies?

It is common knowledge today that certain physical diseases can be triggered by psychological causes. Medicine calls these diseases "psychosomatic" disorders. Think back to the literal sensation of pain in your stomach when you were scared. Marital difficulties can cause migraine, and a broken relationship can trigger diarrhoea. Some researchers even claim to have found psychological factors to be a possible cause of cancer.

On the other hand, psychological factors can `contribute to healing. Do you remember, when you were a little child, running to mummy with your bruised knee? How comforting was her warm embrace and her soothing words; what miracles were worked with an elastoplast! We adults need possibly more complicated forms of treatment but basically, we react like the child with the bruised knee.

About a century ago the first experiments were conducted with *placebos* that is, with tablets containing no active ingredients. The researchers discovered that more important than the substantial effect of many medications is the faith in the effect of the remedy. A physician who prescribes a remedy with great confidence will even have good results with relatively weak pills. Conversely, a usually effective medication can fail when it is prescribed by a critical, terse, and pessimistic doctor.[43] One of the most important curing factors is the physician - so much so that various authors are talking about the "drug called doctor."[44] When there is no confidential relationship between doctor and patient, the use of placebos and homoeopathic remedies is of little avail. But it does not have to be the health practitioner who prescribes the homoeopathic remedy with great conviction, it can be the neighbour or the friend who had tremendous victory over her continual headache.

The *placebo effect* is probably the most important factor in the success of homoeopathic remedies. In fact it may prevent people from taking more dangerous and habit forming drugs. But Christians have to ask themselves: why do we believe so much in homoeopathic pills and tinctures and have so little trust in the caring provision of the Lord? There is a great danger in giving all the honour to the remedy instead of to God who created our bodies! Some, who claim that God has provided the homoeopathic remedies, see no problem there. Yet how can we readily accept that those remedies are from Him?

There is another reason for the success of homoeopathic medicine. A while ago the daughter of an executive told me that her parents had been in a Christian rehabilitation home where they were treated, among other things, with homoeopathic medicine. The cure was very successful and her parents had returned much healthier. My question is: what really helped them?

Dr. Lipross, author of the book *Logic and Magic in Medicine* writes:

> The daily walks, the usual symphony orchestra concert, and many other things which seem unimportant at first glance are at least as crucial for the success of a treatment at a spa as the ritual of baths and drinking the healing water.[45]

In a spa, healing is not facilitated by the homoeopathic remedy, but by the whole *atmosphere*, the *calmness* and the *relaxation*. The medicine only serves the modern superstition of pharmaceutical therapy, to give the guest the impression that he was really "treated."

The least probable factor in a homoeopathic cure is the homoeopathic remedy itself. Organically there is no effect from a remedy in homoeopathic potencies over 6X. And homoeopaths who do not want to dabble in the occult do not exceed this limit.

Occult side-effects of homoeopathy

The healing effect of remedies in higher potencies occurs on a spiritual plane, either through the placebo effect, or through occult powers. In his most important work, the

Organon of Medicine,[46] Samuel Hahnemann explicitly referred to Mesmer's "animal magnetism", "this curative force, often so stupidly denied and disdained for a century." As we have seen, he and his modern followers believed that they convey a cosmic vital force with their potentiated remedies.

Mesmer had been teaching that the healthy person could charge himself with magnetic energy from the earth's magnetic field and in turn heal a sick individual by discharging this energy through the laying on of hands. In his "Palais Mesmer" in Paris, the high society regularly met for magnetic "seances". The sick were gathered in halls lavishly furnished with oriental splendour, holding hands and forming a chain. Rhythmic music emanated from an adjacent room and the tension became electric.

> Then enters Mesmer. He is dressed like an Indian magician. With his slender iron wand he walks around the circle, whispers to his patients, and touches them with the magnetic wand, capturing every patient with his intense stare. Soon one or the other begins to shiver, to scream, laugh, dance or to fall in convulsions. The crisis, intended by Mesmer from the beginning, has occurred![47]

Experience has shown that magnetic healing in this form practically always has to be viewed as an occult practice. Dr. Kurt Koch[48] and other experienced counsellors strongly discourage any contact with "magnetic" healers. Frequently patients who have undergone treatment from "magnetopaths" or "psychic healers" develop psychic abilities themselves.

This is how the former Lutheran pastor, Bolte, got his "gift" of soothsaying - by means of a radionic pendulum.[49] Like many other homoeopaths,[50] he chooses the appropriate remedy for a patient by using the pendulum. In his booklet *From Pendulum Research to Miraculous Healing* he writes:

> I would sit at the desk, take the pendulum
> out, let it circle over Schwabe's list of
> homoeopathic remedies and then order
> the remedy at their pharmacy in Leipzig.

In most instances the pendulum would indicate a
remedy of a high potency.[51]

More than that, Bolte started to "magnetically charge"
whole bottles:

> One thing has remained for emergencies,
> spiritual healing powers captured in
> bottles! In this way you can charge
> ordinary wine or alcohol with spiritual
> energy to make a remedy for certain
> infectous diseases, worms or anything you
> want! This is an art you can teach any
> beginner of spiritistic healing. I have even
> introduced physicians to an effective use
> of these powers . . . [52]

The consequences of such diagnosis and treatment are
described by Dr. Koch. He relates the story of a man who
consulted a psychic healer and took his "magnetically
charged" remedies: "His physical ailment disappeared but
he began to have psychological problems and developed
clairvoyance. The man's son suffered from depression,
blasphemous compulsions and manifold attacks from his
early youth."[53]

Should a Christian take homoeopathic remedies?

Obviously this is a question of conscience everyone has
to answer for himself after reading this book. To avoid
misunderstandings, let me emphasise that not every
homoeopath employs the occult practices which I described
earlier. I have made the acquaintance of physicians and of
health practitioners who, with their homoeopathic
remedies, want nothing else than soft medicine. On the
other hand there are many others who mingle this positive

concern with clearly occult practices.

A former health practitioner and psychic healer wrote to me:

> Satan has a gigantic selection of methods through which he wants to separate man from his salvation in Christ. Some of them are certain 'healing methods', which supposedly bring the patient health. Many Christians are not able to distinguish whether a particular method is covertly infiltrated by the enemy. They fall prey to occult healers, especially when they want to be healed at any price, instead of asking for God's will at any price. . . .
>
> Although the homoeopathic remedy in itself has nothing to do with sorcery . . . it is a fact that many homoeopathic practitioners try to make sure their remedies are working by putting a magic spell on them. It is at this point that such a remedy can serve as a beach head for the enemy and can lead to occult oppression.

This is the opinion of a man who was active as a homoeopath and psychic healer himself. Personally I would not ascribe occult power to the remedy itself. Rather, it is the *faith* of a patient in cosmic healing energies which I would regard as magical. This is why I could not prescribe any homoeopathic remedy after discovering all the information I have compiled in this chapter.

Those Christians who still prescribe them, most of the time, do not realise the background of this method.

I would issue a special warning against all remedies beyond a potency of 6X to 12X, as there is no other explanation for their success than an occult one, or a placebo effect. Furthermore I see spiritual danger in homoeopathic remedies coming from psychic healers and doctors who use the pendulum, practise palmistry, rely on "spiritual energies" or claim to heal at a distance.

However, these practices are not always apparent to the unsuspecting patient. How then should he discern from what source the homoeopathic remedies are coming? Where should we draw the proverbial "line" either to take a homoeopathic remedy or to leave it? As the foundations and the effects of these remedies are dubious anyway, the decision has to be made by the reader himself. It should not be too difficult to do without homoeopathy. There are many herbal remedies which are, without unnecessary dilution, at least as effective in exerting their natural healing power free of undesired side effects.

Seven

Iridology - Diagnoses from the Eyes?

In 1831, Ignaz Peczely, an eleven-year-old Hungarian boy, made his way through the thicket of a large forest. The density of the trees almost cut out the light. It was uncannily silent. Sometimes a deer would start up and flee with long jumps, and then again the silence would only be broken by tiny twigs cracking under Ignaz' feet.

Without Ignaz realising it, he was closely observed by two big yellow eyes. Suddenly a huge something shot out of the dusk. Fear immobilised the boy. Before he could react, an owl had dug her sharp claws into his arm. He had unknowingly come too near to her nest. Ignaz fought desperately against the furious animal. Finally his only way of escape was to break the owl's leg. In the same moment he observed a black line in the owl's eye, running almost perpendicularly downwards in the iris. For a long time after, the boy would ponder on his experience with the owl in the forest. The fracture of the leg, Ignaz concluded, had left a sign in the bird's iris.

Years went by and Peczely, who had first worked as a mechanic, continued his studies to become a natural practitioner and homoeopath. After another four semesters of studies in Vienna he was awarded with the degree of a Medical Doctor. One day, he observed in a patient's iris a line, and was immediately reminded of his experience with the owl. In the same way as the fracture had caused a black sign in the owl's eye, other diseases would also leave their mark in the eyes, he concluded.[1] Iridology was born.

Peczely started to subdivide the iris into 12 sectors and correlated each sector with various organs of the body. Thus, the zone directly lying around the black pupil was supposed to indicate diseases of the stomach. The legs found their reflection in zones 6 and 7 whereas the organs of the head could be seen in the upper zones of the iris. In this way, the whole anatomy was finally projected on the eyes. Almost at the same time, other herbalists and homoeopaths started to look at and use the eyes as a diagnostic aid.

The spotlight of publicity really turned on iridology at the turn of the century, through the trial of naturopath and iridologist Felke, also dubbed "a clay pastor."[2] In one year alone he had treated 15,000 patients. Although he claimed that iridology was infallible and would never err, he failed completely. The jury asked him to establish the diagnosis in twenty selected patients. These are the "diseases" which he found in a man with syphilis:

> Pupils not regular, probably worm-infested. Drinks good chicken-soup and good coffee, dreams a lot at night, has cold feet, high blood pressure, general aches combined with back-pain, must have jumped hard on his legs at one time in his life, has a tendency towards migraine, stomach aches and gall-stones.

But he did not discover the real disease. In the same way he failed with the other 19 patients.

Iridology however started its triumphal entry into the world of the superstitious.

The eye - opening of the liver?

When a Chinese doctor, 4000 years ago, examined a patient, he would use a kind of iridology.[3] In the same way as the destiny of small man was dependent on the constellation of the stars in the infinite universe, according to Chinese thinking, the organs of the big world of man would be reflected in the small world of the eye: *microcosm* reflected *macrocosm*.

For the Chinese, the iris was the opening of the liver. A close examination would reveal all disorders of the liver.

There was even more to see: the upper eyelid related to the spleen, the lower to the stomach. The white of the eye showed diseases of the lungs, the black pupil in the centre those of the kidney. The inner corner of the eye related to the heart, whereas the outer indicated the condition of the digestive system.

Paracelsus, the great authority behind the scenes of the modern movement of "natural medicine", regarded the eye as microcosm and man as macrocosm, establishing links with astrology. [4] The interrelatedness of macrocosm and microcosm does not only form the basis of astrology, but also of palmistry, magic, acupuncture and reflexology. And this teaching was not less prominent among the naturopaths of Ignaz Peczely's days than it is today.

Astrologer Libra, who lived in the 19th century, wrote the following under the theme "Zodiac of the Eye":

> Why is it that everything that happens in the body, has to find its expression in the eye? For the same reason, as everything that goes on in the universe, is happening in man. The eye reflects the cosmos of the human body from the point of its birth, and it registers all changes that have happened since. It is unnecessary to point out that this reflection could equally take place in any other part of the body, but the iris is best suited for this purpose. [5]

An interview with Dr. Bernard Jensen, one of the best known iridologists in America, gives us valuable insight into contemporary thinking among iridologists. Asked how he would relate astrology to his studies in iridology, Dr. Jensen answered:

> Because astrology has its effect on the body, and the condition of the body is revealed in the iris of the eye, we find that various organs work in harmony with the influence existing at birth - the influence

> with which we came into this world. For
> instance, people who are waterlogged or
> who have lymphatic gland congestions
> tend to hold water in their bodies. By
> looking at their charts, we see that they are
> greatly influenced by the water signs. [6]

Many iridologists are embarrassed and deny the background of their art, trying instead to make their work respectable with a multitude of pseudo-scientific explanations. The fact is that iridology constitutes a diagnostic method on the grounds of Eastern philosophy and magic conceptions.

The miracle of the eye

The human eye is one of the most wonderful organs of our body. Only about as big as a golf ball, it conveys to us the most beautiful sensation we know: the colourful world of light and forms around us; the bright red of roses, the azure of the sea, the tender green of spring. 6 million cones (for colour vision) and 120 million rods (black-and-white vision) are found in the retina of one eye alone. The information they receive is processed and stored in the brain. In the eyeball itself a wonderfully sophisticated system makes sure that - despite most extreme variations of light conditions - always the proper amount of light is falling on the retina.

One central part of this system is the *iris*. If it is strongly coloured, the eyes appear to be brown; when there is little pigment, the eyes are blue. We inherit the colour of our eyes from our parents. Through the finely tuned activities of the papillary muscle the pupil becomes wide in darkness and it contracts to the size of a pinhead in the bright light of the sun. To be able to sustain these constant movements, the iris is constructed with tiny elements meshing like a sponge, similar to the lamellas of a camera's lens. Depending on the light angle, these lamellas form various patterns. As each person has his or her characteristic finger print, the appearance of our eyes is unique for each individual, but it has *no further significance*. To try and read diseases from these patterns and the colours is as hopeless as to attempt to determine from a criminal's fingerprints if he ever broke a leg.

What can a doctor see in the eye? Obviously a detailed examination would reveal diseases of the eyes themselves. But here we are especially interested in general diseases of the body that would be expressed in changes of the eye.

Let's start with the white of the eye called the sclera. It is generally known that jaundice usually shows up first in the white of the eye. The reason lies in the fact that the yellow colour of bile can be seen best on a white background, although it is equally deposited in the rest of the body's skin which is somewhat darker. The symptom of "jaundice" can indicate a wide variety of disorders: a harmless irregularity of the metabolism or a malignant tumour of the pancreas; difficulties of the liver in processing a drug (often the "pill") or the inflammation of the liver through a virus (hepatitis). The list could be continued for many pages to cover all conditions that cause a yellow colour of the skin. Much less common than yellow sclera are blue ones which only occur with a rare condition of brittle bones.

The transparent cornea can be affected through a virus (usually the Herpes virus). Moreover, it is very sensitive to dehydration or relatively slight injuries. Often, a little ulceration would occur; the remaining scar is white and non-transparent which leads to an impairment of vision. Many older people have a grey ring around the cornea which is made up of a harmless pigment-deposit.

The lens of the eye can also be involved in a general disease. The lack of certain vitamins or the ingestion of medications can lead to a turbidity of the lens, thus impairing vision. Severe changes of the lens can occur in babies whose mothers had German measles in the first months of pregnancy.

Of special importance for the physician is the examination of the "fundus", the inner lining of the rear part of the eye. Here he not only can observe the *retina*, but also the optic nerve and the eye's blood vessels. The arteries give an indication of such important general diseases as high blood pressure and diabetes. The optic nerve can be changed for instance in cases of a brain tumour causing an increase in pressure of the cerebro-spinal fluid.

Finally, let's turn to the *iris*, the coloured membrane of the eye, from which iridologists want to read so much. It can be involved in an inflammation of the eye's inner lining and is then swollen and discoloured in a greenish tone. The reasons for such an inflammation can lie in infectious foci, such as tuberculosis, venereal diseases or rare forms of arthritis. In all these conditions there have to be further general symptoms to confirm the diagnosis.

As a physician it would be sheer presumption to read more out of the eyes than that.

Liver-degeneration or little finger?

The activities of an iridologist cannot be seriously compared to a physician's examination; the term "iris-interpretation" would better describe them than the scientific sounding "iridology". Prof. Schreck, M.D., a renowned ophthalmologist, comments:

> The iris-interpreters employ a completely different and in no way comparable examination technique. They claim to 'see' diseases of the human body from normal tissue by simply looking at its surface. [7]

He continues:

> We have here a grotesque, absurd paradox, unique in all of medical history, that these people want to read diseases out of completely normal tissue. Worse still, they do not even refer to disorders of this tissue itself but to diseases of organs that are far from it, and in no way related in any way with the iris...
> What the iris-interpreters refer to and where they claim to 'see' bodily diseases,

is nothing else than simple variations of
the normal structure and colouring of the
iris that carry no pathological significance
and therefore have no value for diagnosis.

Although every iris-interpreter tells the patient that there
was only one diagnostic key, one author has counted no
less than 19 different iridology charts. According to the
various charts, the same small area between 230 and 240
degrees - an area of the width of a pin - can indicate
disorders of the following organs: the liver, the little finger,
the arm, the diaphragm, the hand, the ribs, the axillary
lymphnodes and the gall-bladder. [8]

It is estimated that there are about 10,000 diseases. It is
not clear how they would all find their reflection in the tiny
space of the iris.

Scientific investigations

As a diagnosis from the iris could replace many
expensive tests, the claims of the iris-interpreters have been
checked in many serious studies. Let us look at a few
results.

A good starting point are Peczely's original *observations*
of the owl. It would be easy to demonstrate a change in the
eye by taking a photograph before and after breaking of a
leg. However, this could never be accomplished. Iridology
in its modern form was started through the *error of its
inventor*. In 1957, researcher Dr. Woehlisch was able to
reconstruct what the eleven-year-old Ignaz had actually
seen. He observed that the black inner lining of the upper
lid is slightly lagging behind the lid when the owl opens her
eyes. The observer then gets the impression that a dark line,
almost perpendicular, slowly moves over the light iris. The
photographs are so convincing that this explanation is
probably accurate.[9]

Another physician[10] examined 762 patients with very
severe diseases, among them 60 army veterans many of
whom had had an amputation. He proved conclusively that
iridology was invalid. Among the 762 patients only 18 (that

is 2.7 percent) had a sign in the area that the iridology chart assigned to the affected organ. More than 50 percent, however, had pathological signs in areas of organs that had never been involved. The same investigator made a test with one of the most prominent iris-interpreters of his time which was witnessed by several doctors and laymen. Iridologist Klaeser was asked to diagnose patients with severe ailments and mutilations that were obvious even to medical laymen. After eight attempts the experiment was discontinued as the "famous" man had given nothing but wrong diagnoses. In a patient with an amputated leg, for instance, he found only a "marked congestion of the spinal cord."

Very revealing were the results of a study conducted at the Veterans Administration Medical Centre at San Diego, California. [11] Three ophthalmologists and three iridologists were asked to find out, from the iris only, if a given patient had a kidney disease or not. Iridologists had claimed they could diagnose this condition easily. The results were shattering: the worth of the diagnoses was not higher than random guesses. One iridologist had the astonishing rate of 88 percent correct diagnoses in patients with kidney disease. It turned out, however, that he also labeled 88 percent of the healthy people as having kidney disease. Thus, the art of faulty diagnoses paves the way to highly successful cures through homoeopathy and herbal medicine. It is easy to cure non-existing conditions!

The list of scientific studies could be continued. Iridologists have not been able to sustain their claims with diagnostic success in one single objective research-study.

Why then are there so many correct diagnoses?

A woman told me her story:

> Many years ago I went to see an iridologist, because my work at that time had become too heavy for me and I felt constantly drained and tired. He told me that I was basically healthy but needed

> relaxation and vitamins. However, 'out of
> the blue', he found that my gall-bladder
> was weak and instructed me to go easy on
> it. He gave me herbal pills that helped me
> with my digestion. A few years later I
> went for a routine-check-up where a
> physician found a mild jaundice, probably
> due to an inborn defect.

Like many others, this patient was stunned when she realised that the iris-interpreter had found this jaundice already years ago. In her case, however, the reason is not difficult to find: an innate (or congenital) jaundice shows up as a yellow colouring on the white sclera as has been already described. The iridologist had, in this case, not made his diagnosis from the structure of the iris, but - like the physician - observed the discolouring of the conjunctiva.

Therefore, the first reason for diagnostic success is a *good observation* of the patients. Moreover, most patients tell their iridologists their whole medical story and the symptoms they are having, thus giving enough clues to make a diagnosis before even looking at the iris.

Secondly, mark the *vague terminology* of the iridologists. What does it mean when "the gall-bladder is weak"? As you might know, there are various possibilities for a gall-bladder to be diseased, eg. stones, inflammation, or a tumour. In the case of this lady, it wasn't the gall-bladder at all, but - strictly medically speaking - it was a build up of bile in the blood, due to a harmless metabolic disorder affecting the liver.

Thirdly, most iridologists do not give a single diagnosis but *a whole list*. One example is the litany of "clay-pastor" Felke on page 84. Even a short glance over the "diagnoses" shows that he had to be right somewhere: who does not dream a lot in the night? Who doesn't have cold feet at times, who has never had back ache?

The more darts you throw at a dart board, the higher the probability that you will hit the bull's eye. And should the interpreter be completely off-target, there is one especially convincing explanation: either he has seen signs in the iris that point to diseases of the parents or the grandparents, or the sign is an indication that there is a "weakness" of the organ, that could perhaps lead to a manifestation of disease in the future.

To make the list complete we have to mention a fourth reason for accurate diagnoses where the harmless and amusing variety of tricks finds a sudden end. We have to consider the possibility of an *occult iris-diagnosis through psychic influences*, but this is rather rare.

Ophthalmologist Dr Jaensch writes:

> Although it cannot be denied that occasionally clairvoyance is playing a role in iridology, or that the iridologist as a psychic taps the subconscious of the patient, we have to realise that mediums using iridology are very rare; certainly not all iridologists are psychics. [12]

There seem to be some occult iridologists whose diagnoses are often hitting home. These "iris-clairvoyants" as I would call them, according to Dr. Koch, "are psychic and work with various forms of psychic power. The iris is just one *contact bridge* which can be used for the tapping of the conscious or subconscious mind through telepathy, clairvoyance, or trance."[13]

This leads us right into the next question:

Does iridology lead to occult bondage?

According to the experience of various counsellors, certainly not every iris-"diagnosis" leads to occult bondage. Dr. Koch writes:

> There are psychic, occult methods of diagnosis. In order not to give rise to any misunderstandings, I must say that there are few occult iridologists. Many iridologists have nothing to do with the

> occult. The medical value of their
> diagnosis, however is extraordinarily thin.
> In many cases it is meaningless.[14]

The minority of iridologists who work using occult powers, should be warning enough to stay clear. The title of an "M.D." is no guarantee for a "neutral" iris-interpretation. In his *Occult ABC*, Koch mentions that he had counselled physicians who confessed their occult practices, and subsequently gave them up.

There is no point in asking how to discern which practitioners and physicians use iridology in an occult way. Trying to find out from the iridologist himself probably will not prove helpful.

The question rather is, can a patient safely use a diagnostic method that not only builds on occult philosophy but also on the error of its inventor?

Eight

Radiesthesia - Healing and Prevention with the Pendulum?

Cancer is probably mankind's most terrible scourge. One out of three persons in the Western world will some day die of cancer.

Specialists as well as laymen are at a loss to know what causes a group of cells to run suddenly wild, or how to effectively counter this devouring Moloch. Despite heavily funded prevention programmes, modern surgical techniques, and huge radiation-canons, the overall mortality due to this fearful disease has not decreased - although partial success can be claimed with a few tumours.

Death-bringing radiations?

Whenever something cannot be explained, there is a massive growth of theories and hypotheses. Today we are confronted with a multitude of speculations surrounding the origins of cancer and how to heal it: from laetrile to imaging techniques. To find one's way around in this jungle of ideas is almost impossible.

The attempt to explain cancer has long ceased to be the limited domain of physicians and scientists. Increasingly, laymen and self-made "specialists" are publishing their views of how to conquer this disease. These views are receiving widespread publicity from tabloids and magazines. One of the theories proposes that cancer, and a long list of other diseases, is purportedly caused by underground *water veins* and *emanations*,[1] also known as *"cold spots"*.

Dowsers claim that they can locate these underground water veins. In fact over half a million water wells have been located by dowsers in the U.S. alone. Dowsers explain that they do this by means of a green willow twig which is attracted to water in the ground. However, much more is involved than a simple twig, as we shall see later.

According to Stanley Krysiak, a Canadian dowser, 90% of the following diseases "are caused by noxious radiations: circulation problems, various forms of cancer, suicide, retarded children, mental disorders, arthritis and rheumatism, diabetes, diseases of the digestive system (including liver and kidneys), blindness and skin-rashes."[2] So convinced is he that he states: "Medical science will not see any substantial progress in the healing of these diseases unless it recognises the death-bringing underground emanations."

These surprising insights are supported by stories like the following: "Dr. Birkelbach told me about a maid who was serving in a rich mansion. She seemed to be happy and liked by all, but one day she tried to hang herself. She was saved just in time and brought to the hospital. In an unobserved moment she escaped and hanged herself again. This time help came too late." A dowser was called, and his investigation revealed - not surprisingly - noxious emanations under the maid's bed. Other causes were not even taken into consideration.[3]

In another report, the poor achievement of 2000 children in Salzburg, Austria was attributed to noxious radiations. An undergraduate teacher tested the homes of the children whose learning zeal had worn off. Together with 70 dowsers she concluded "that students become lethargic when they sit over water veins in school, or are under the influence of noxious emanations while sleeping at home."[4] Again, there was no mention of other causes, such as social difficulties at home, or of environmental factors; not to mention the fact that every student has periods of the blues at times. The solution is much simpler: all problems are explained by the presence of noxious water veins.

The publications of dowsers and their societies are full of similar articles, based on pseudo-scientific "research" and strange anecdotes. Only fantasy sets the limits for the variety of explanations, such as: "The battle between a human organ and bacteria is in reality a war between incoming and outgoing waves." [5] Every cell-type is supposed to have its own particular wavelength. The noxious radiations from underground water veins disturb the balance of these microwaves, thus causing disease, especially cancer."

There is no unity among dowsers themselves. In an article in the East/West Journal, Alex Comb writes: "There seem to be as many theories as to why a dowsing rod should work as there are dowsers to think them up." [6]

The latest in-word is borrowed from physics: "microwaves." We are familiar with microwaves as used in cooking or in the radar-systems of airport control towers. Similarly, the FM waves of radio and TV are microwaves. Although all these waves are measureable with scientific instruments, the microwaves which supposedly cause cancer are different. They are said to be picked up only by the dowsing rod or the radionic pendulum, and are too weak to be measured by physical devices.

This immediately raises the question: How can a dowser, in the midst of all the microwaves surrounding us, feel exactly those waves which are too weak to be measured in any other way? Until today this question has gone unanswered by the dowsers. They admit themselves that research is not able to solve this riddle. [7]

A charm in the bedroom

That their claims are resting on an Eastern-occult basis does not hinder dowsers and gadget-quacks from selling their patients various devices to counter the noxious radiations. Professor of Forensic Medicine, Dr. Prokop, has compiled a list of fifty different "radionic devices". [9] You would not believe the things people use to ward off noxious radiations. [8] Here are a few examples I found in the American and British literature: Mu-metal, copper spirals and screens, aluminium foils, metal bars, fibreglass tape (which is supposedly more effective if coloured blue) etc.

Some boxes contain wires, switches and batteries to make them look more sophisticated. Customers are warned not to open the box lest its effect be rendered useless. What they would really discover is that the wires go around in senseless circles, ending blindly in a corner. The prices for these devices are outrageous, often four to ten times the actual value of the material. But people are ready to pay absurd sums to regain the sleep they haven't had for so long, or to protect themselves from cancer.

The function of his box is explained in different ways by every dowser. Some are supposed to generate anti-waves dissolving the microwaves that are emanated from the ground and the universe. Others act like a shield, intercepting the noxious emanations before they hit their victim. None is able to explain in terms of physics how they work, and when pressed for answers, dowsers retreat to their Eastern-occult world-view to justify their actions.

In an excellent article on *The Gadget Quacks*,[10] Wallace Janssen describes several "radionic" devices that were widely used in the U.S. Like the dowser's deradiation boxes, they claimed to diagnose and to heal a wide variety of diseases, including cancer.

In the 1920's Dr. Albert Abrams invented a system of machines in which a dry specimen of blood could be inserted, and a diagnosis established by its special micro-radiation. Local practitioners, most of whom were chiropractors, then received a postcard telling them the diagnosis and giving advice regarding which wavelength should be used to treat their patients.

When FDA agents investigated the system, they arranged to send the dried blood of an 11-week-old rooster. This resulted in a report of sinus infection and bad teeth. Nonetheless, a British committee under chairman Sir Thomas Horder "admitted that Abram's claims for the diagnostic value of his methods were valid."[11]

Later, a Los Angeles Chiropractor, Ruth Drown, built similar machines, which supposedly were able to "tune in" to specific organs of the body. With the help of a little black box and two blood spots, she claimed to be able to treat a patient by remote control anywhere in the world. One of her many tragic victims was a woman treated for breast cancer with the Drown device until the tumour was too advanced for successful surgery.

Still famous and accepted among Holistic Health practitioners is Wilhelm Reich, M.D., one-time pupil of psychiatrist Sigmund Freud. Reich claimed to have discovered "orgone-energy" which he called "the most powerful force in the universe." Although never confirmed by scientific research, Reich even found ways to accumulate the energy in a black box, built of wood, metal and insulation board, about the size of a telephone booth. Sitting in the box was supposed to charge the blood with vital energy and thus cure diseases including cancer. Chiropractors, physicians and laymen bought the boxes by the hundreds, renting them to patients for 250 dollars a month. Eventually the hoax was forbidden by the American Food and Drug Administration. But to this day British and European practitioners hail the device as a very important discovery. [12] Orgone energy is regarded as a biological energy and described as "identical to the life-energy that the Hindus call *prana.*"

In recent years new radionic instruments have been developed, such as the "Base 44 radionic instrument" with an impressive number of 44 switches and knobs. Chiropractor David Tansley, who describes himself as "well versed in the Eastern concepts of the chakras and the subtle anatomy of man," gives this description of radionic diagnosis and treatment:

> It is a basic tenet of radionics that man, as well as all life-forms, shares a common field of energy, and that each individual has his own particular surrounding energy field, some aspects of which are electromagnetic. If this field should become sufficiently distorted, then ultimately disease will manifest itself in the organism at a physical level.
>
> In radionics, all diseases, organs and remedies are seen to have their own

special frequency or vibration. These can be expressed in numerical values known as 'rates'; hence the calibrated dials of the radionic instruments upon which the frequencies or 'rates' can be placed for diagnostic or treatment purposes.

When a radionic practitioner makes a health analysis for a patient he utilises the principles of dowsing by applying the faculties of extrasensory perception (ESP) to the process of detecting disease . . .[13]

When dowsers are tested

Although dowsers have compiled an impressive record of pseudo-scientific data,[14] the mechanism of their art is not clear to themselves.[15] A layman in the field of physics might imagine that the movement of the rod or the pendulum was somehow being influenced by electric waves or magnetic energy. However, repeated tests under objective control have not supported this idea. We have already mentioned the problem of microwaves and seen that the claims of the dowsers cannot be verified. Moreover, a magnetic field cannot be sensed by human organs. In 1954, a test in the Netherlands exposed dowsers to magnetic fields which were all stronger than the natural magnetic field of the earth. None of the testpersons was able to indicate when a magnetic field was switched on or when it was off.[16] Another theory proposes a type of "water radiation." If that is the case, why is it only underground water that emits this radiation and not the water on the surface?

How is it possible, physically, that a "water vein" (this term does not exist in geology) emits its radiation in such a concentrated beam that a dowser can still trace it on the twentieth floor of a high-rise building? Why does the physical principle of dispersion not apply here?

Dowsers have failed to give an answer, hiding behind a wall of anecdotal reports, the names of Sirs, Lords, professors and scientists, and an unorganised array of terms that have been borrowed from physical sciences. "Dowsing" is being replaced by the much more scientific label of "Radiesthesia" exerting an enormous impression on the average layman.

Less impressed are those who have tested and compared the achievements of various dowsers. Here is the result of a controlled experiment with 75 dowsers in New Zealand: "No agreement, same results could be obtained with guessing." [17] Most of the time there are as many waterveins as there are dowsers looking for them.

Equally disappointing are the results of a study conducted by Prof. Gassmann at the renowned *Federal Technical Institute* of Zurich, Switzerland.[18] He wanted to investigate the radiation which was purportedly measured by the dowsers. 16 well-known and experienced dowsers volunteered for the test. Among them were 11 engineers and technicians, one of them even a university professor. To find a strong radiation source, Professor Gassmann sent the 16 dowsers to 7 fields and asked them to localise the underground water-pipe running under each of them. The largest pipe carried as much as 4000 gallons per minute.

When the drawings of the 16 dowsers were compared, the results were shattering:

> It is obvious that there are no areas of radiation clearly separated from a neutral background, on which the dowsers could agree... The goal of the tests... was not accomplished...
>
> Despite intensive research we did not find any criteria that would allow us to accept the findings of any of the dowsers as accurate or even as more reliable than the others. The large pipe was not found by any of them, several dowsers reported water pipes in places where there were none (on field B obviously influenced by a visible manhole lid). We were not successful, with the help of the methods described, in localising any sources of

radiation that would have helped in further investigations.

How do the rod and pendulum work?

Despite those multiple negative experiments, the riddle of rod and pendulum is still unsolved. Their activity is a reality that cannot be pushed aside.

If the power which moves rod and pendulum cannot be measured physically, where do the movements come from? What is the power influencing the dowsers? Why is it that not every one is sensitive to the pendulum? Why is it that a novice will suddenly get the "gift" when touched by an experienced dowser?

These questions demand an answer. Scientists have proposed various hypotheses as to why the radionic pendulum reacts in the hand of a dowser:

1. Although dowsers claim to keep their hands absolutely motionless when the pendulum starts to move, they still have *subtle muscular twitches*. One researcher[19] has investigated the factors that lead to minimal muscular vibrations even when the hand is kept absolutely still. These twitches are not only caused by the muscles themselves, and by the pulses in the finger-tips, but also as the result of thought-patterns in the *brain*.

Anyone who has used a gun knows how impossible it is, despite enormous will-power, to keep bead and notch in line without any movement. The longer one hesitates, the more nervous one becomes, and the more the gun subtly trembles.

In the same way, say the scientists, the internal tension in the dowser approaches a climax which, without conscious effort, suddenly releases the willow twig.

2. Dowsers are *good observers* and rely on clues to produce their results. Thus, a manhole-lid usually points to some sort of water-pipe or drain. The observation of such a clue is supposed to release the mental tension in the dowser and to cause the movement of the rod.

3. *Suggestion and Auto-Suggestion:* most dowsers diagnose "water veins" and "cold spots" when they are aware that someone has died in a particular bed or when a cow has been sick in a stable. The thought then releases the answer through the pendulum or rod. Dr. Reimann writes: "The hand is, in a sense, only the finger of the psychological and emotional clockwork of the dowser."[20]

Suggestion and Auto-suggestion probably account to a large extent, for the "healing power" of radionic boxes and orgone-accumulators. Psychosomatic factors play a major role also (see chapter 10). When the faith in the device ebbs away, the same old arthritic pains come back.

All these theories demonstrate one crucial fact: *It is not a physically measurable power that moves the dowsers' instruments but the power of the subconscious mind, the power of the spirit.*

Absolute spiritual passivity

There is one factor which all these scientific theories do not include: *The susceptibility of the human mind to occult and demonic forces.* Writing on the topic of *The spiritual attitude of the dowser,* a dowser gives the following advice: "We can only obtain objective results when we remain in *absolute passivity of mind".*[21] Another author says : "Only an attitude which is *absolutely unprejudiced in every case* can yield regular successful results."[22] (italics mine). In other words: if you honestly pray you cannot use the radionic pendulum, because you are no longer unprejudiced.

Spiritual passivity is the goal of every form of yoga and Eastern meditation. It is not surprising, therefore, to find Eastern-occult concepts throughout the publications of the dowsers and radionic practitioners. Dowsing is explained as man's ability "to bring his life into conformity with those energies and forces that are in the universe and make their impact upon man and his environment."[23] This is an allusion to the old principle of the relationship between macrocosm and microcosm already encountered in acupuncture, reflexology and iridology.

Dowsing "is linked to some kind of psychic energy, and interconnected universal life force," writes Comb.[24] People "open up to a firsthand, practical encounter with psychic energy or spirit. Dowsing is a spiritual discipline, although it involves no dogma or set of beliefs, no theories, initiations, or ceremonies." He continues: "Dowsing requires concentration. The best way to achieve this is either to repeat the questions you ask of the rod over and over in your mind like a yogi repeating a mantra, or to ask the question just once and then allow your mind to go blank. It can be that simple."

It is a well known fact that spiritual passivity carries with it the risk that powers beyond a person's control may take over the mind. Transcendental Meditation and other forms of Yoga have led to severe personality changes. With the help of the "mantra", meditators create a state of absolute spiritual vulnerability which can eventually bring them into bondage and demonic oppression.[25] The danger of spiritual passivity is also demonstrated in *hypnosis*: quite a few spiritistic mediums first discovered their ability after having undergone a hypnotic trance.[26]

A *"machine that a ghost could operate"* was how Nobel-laureate and internationally renowned brain researcher, Sir John Eccles, described the human brain.[27] Dave Hunt, internationally recognised authority on cults and psychic phenomena, explains:

> Normally, my mind is the 'ghost' that operates my brain. But if I enter an altered state of consciousness and allow what a psychic or meditator calls a cosmic force, or the medium calls a spirit control or guide, to take over, there would seem to be nothing to prevent this other mind from becoming the new "ghost" operating my brain, creating experiences that would seem very real to me but were not actually taking place.[28]

Spiritual passivity is also a requirement for "the training

of spiritistic mediums," as described by spiritualist Johannes Greber: [29]

> One starts with a short prayer, reads a portion from the Holy Scriptures and meditates over it. Then he puts his hand with a loosely held pencil on a sheet of paper and waits *without any tension of the mind*. When he feels urged to write out ideas that are inspired with a strong sense of determination, he should write them down. When he feels his hand being moved by a foreign power, he should *yield*.

Mark the religious framework of these instructions to develop psychic abilities! Not everyone who uses Christian vocabulary has his gifts from God.[30] This is equally true for dowsers who honestly believe they have received their "gift" from God. Watchman Nee writes: "After one's mind has sunk into passivity he will receive many thoughts injected from without, notions which are unclean, blasphemous or confused."[31]

Radiesthesia - the science of divination

A former dowser who was converted, writes:

> It is amazing how skilled Satan is in camouflaging his activities, so as to enthrall, under the banner of science, even the 'scholars'. The radionic pendulum is nothing more than an *instrument of divination*. [32] The spirit that takes over the mind of the passive dowser is a divining spirit as described in the Bible.[33]

A closer look at dowsing reveals that dowsers are not really measuring any radiation at all. Says Dave Hunt: [34]

Recent developments, however, have made nonsense of that kind of explanation. During the Viet Nam War, for instance, U.S. soldiers located secret Viet Cong tunnels and underground ammunition dumps using dowsing rods made of coathangers and anything else that was handy.

The eye-opener comes when you realise that highly developed dowsers can do this thing over a map. The major water sources on the island of Bermuda, for instance, were pinpointed in this way, after geologists had checked out the place and concluded there was no water and no point in drilling for any. A dowser, sitting over a map of Bermuda in Kennebunkport, Maine, a thousand miles from the place itself, located three well sites. The government of Bermuda drilled on those spots and found the water that still supplies Bermuda today.

Similarly, in Medical Radiesthesia, the dowser could not measure any vibration but could ask questions, a clear case of divination. The famous Abbe Mermet, when examining an animal or a human subject for disease, asked the following questions: [35]

1. Is any organ affected by disease?

2. If so, which one?

3. Which part of the organ, and if possible, where is the precise seat of the trouble?

4. What is the nature of the disease? To what extent has it progressed?

Radiesthesia is used in the same way in order to choose

the "proper" homoeopathic remedy[36] for a particular patient. It is no exaggeration to say that the dowser's question-answer ritual is *no different from the use of the Ouija-board.*

Sensitivity to the rod and the pendulum is, according to Christian expert and counsellor Dr. Kurt Koch, based on psychic powers[37] which are "often found in the proximity to sins of sorcery." How is it possible to acquire such powers? Dr. Koch comments:

> The gift of using the rod or discovering secret knowledge by means of the pendulum can be acquired in three ways: by heredity, by transference from a powerful occultist, or by experimenting with magic formulas as they are described in occult books.

Thus, the treatment by a radionic practitioner can lead to extrasensory perception and psychic powers.

This phenomenon was described by former Lutheran pastor and later occultist J. Bolte. He started to experiment with a pendulum following a description in the newspaper, and discovered to his surprise that he was sensitive to its movements. He concluded:

> It seemed that I was one of those so-called psychics who have enough orgone energy in themselves. Only later did I realise that I did not possess this ability from birth. Shortly before I had been very ill and was treated by a well-known magnetic healer. Undoubtedly, I became magnetic through his treatment, and was now able to use the pendulum through this power. Thus, magnetic treatment can make anybody magnetic who is willing and has a pure heart, and thus can enable him to use the radionic pendulum.[38]

What should a Christian do when he discovers psychic powers in himself which enable him for instance to use the rod? Dr. Koch says: "If a Christian discovers he has a psychic disposition, he should ask God to take it away. The idea of some theologians that psychic powers can be purified and then used in the service of God's kingdom is unscriptural. This is illustrated by the story of the fortuneteller of Philippi in Acts 16: 16-18. If a Christian uses psychic powers, he is committing sin and is in need of forgiveness."[39]

A spirit of prostitution leads them astray

Rod and pendulum are ancient forms of divination. It is therefore not surprising that the Scriptures comment on the practice. The prophet Hosea laments: "They consult a wooden idol and are answered by a stick of wood. A spirit of prostitution leads them astray; they are unfaithful to their God."[40] The original words for "wooden idol" and "stick" correspond to early forms of divining rods.

Moses charges the people of Israel in the name of God: "Do not turn to mediums or seek out spiritists, for you will be defiled by them : I am the Lord your God."[41] And further: "Let no one be found among you... who practises divination or sorcery, interprets omens, engages in witchcraft, or casts spells, or who is a medium or spiritist or who consults the dead. Anyone who does these things is detestable to the Lord." [42]

These clear commands cannot be watered down, even when some people claim that they are doing good with the help of the rod. Other Christian leaders try to explain that psychic abilities are perhaps part of our human potential which should be developed. People ask: "Hasn't the well in a Theological Seminary in Europe been found by the means of dowsing? Aren't there evangelists who have worked with the pendulum and peddled de-radiation boxes?" That might be true, but the honest desire of many dowsers to do good with their "gift", though commendable, does not invalidate the clear guidelines of the Bible.

Jesus warned his disciples that in the last times there

would be false prophets, performing "great signs and miracles to deceive even the elect - if that were possible."[43]

In another instance, Jesus speaks of the great and terrible day when the truth shall be revealed:

> Many will say to me on that day, 'Lord, Lord, did we not prophesy in your name, and in your name drive out demons and perform many miracles?' Then I will tell them plainly, ' I never knew you. Away from me, you evildoers!'[44]

A further indication that the "gift " of dowsing is not from God is the fact that *honest prayer makes the use of the rod impossible.* A former dowser tells this story:

> I had always had very good results with the pendulum. To me my special sensitivity was a gift from God, and I tried to explain the movements as a result of magnetic fields. I had prayed a lot about the practice. When I started to have failures with radionic devices, I started having doubts and began to wonder: could it be that the enemy was behind the whole thing?
> I began to pray with deep sincerity, asking the Lord to give me complete clarity in the matter. I prayed: 'Lord show me if the oscillations of the pendulum are Your work or from below. If the movements are not from You, don't let the pendulum move any longer in my hands...' The result: the pendulum abruptly stopped. I tried to get it swinging over two spots in my house where it had always given strong reactions, but since that prayer it did not work anymore.[45]

Deceiving powers

"The idols speak deceit. Diviners see visions that lie, they tell dreams that are false. They give comfort in vain."[46] If "radionic boxes" replaced the word "idols", and "dowsers" the word "diviners", one could not better describe the situation than Zechariah did. In antiquity, as today, innumerable people who rely on superstition are blantantly deceived. The prophet Micah knew the situation, too: "... her prophets tell fortunes for money. Yet they lean upon the Lord and say, 'Is the Lord among us?'"[47]

Many a reaction of a dowsing rod is prompted not so much by a magnetic field but by the chequebook of the inquirer. It is no contradiction to describe the unreliability of dowsing in the first part of this chapter, and the dark powers involved in the second part. Satan works with powers that deceive. Thus Paul warns the church of "the coming of the lawless one" which will be "in accordance with the work of Satan displayed by all kinds of counterfeit miracles, signs and wonders, and every sort of evil that deceives those who are perishing."[48]

Patients who open themselves to these powers by having their house examined by a dowser or by installing radionic devices are clearly venturing into the area of the occult. They may in some cases experience physical improvement, but risk emotional and spiritual trouble, especially when they have been rather sensitive before getting in contact with such practices.

Such inner tensions may be a warning signal, but *deliverance* is possible by clearly giving up these occult involvements. I would strongly encourage one to do so in the presence of an experienced and spiritually minded pastor-counsellor. When you have been involved in practices described in this chapter, ask Jesus to forgive you for having relied more on divination and radionic charms than on His sufficiency. Consciously rededicate your life to Him and you can be sure that He will deliver you from all occult bondage. You can rest in Him even if you might have to continue to live with physical and psychological weakness.

Nine

Herbal Medicine - Those Healing Plants

The last two decades have seen a gigantic increase in the use of herbal medicine. In 1977 alone, 10,000 tons of herbs were sold in Germany, up from 50 tons twenty years earlier. The "Green Sweep", as it has been called, has also reached the United States, where sales of herbal products have jumped from nearly nothing a decade ago to a market value in 1979 of at least 150 million dollars.[1]

Most of the products are in the form of herbal teas for such conditions as bronchitis, insomnia or kidney and bladder complaints. An increasing number of people are trying to avoid the ingrained habit of taking "chemicals" when they suffer, for example, from bronchitis. They would rather brew themselves a soothing bronchial tea, directly from the pharmacy God has created in nature.

The most ancient remedies in history

No remedies are as old as the healing herbs. They have been used for the treatment of disease in all cultures, be they highly developed or desperately primitive. The ancient Egyptian Papyrus Ebers contains 900 prescriptions.[2] The *Egyptians* were familiar with about one third of all remedies which are listed in modern pharmaceutical books. They not only used juniper, garlic, fennel, thyme, castor oil and many other herbal preparations, but also the opium poppy which originally served to produce the painkilling drugs morphia and codeine.

The ancient peoples of *Mexico* had an equally impressive treasury of healing herbs. In a voluminous work on the *Natural History of the New World*, the royal Spanish Physician for the West Indies, Dr. Francisco Hernandez, compiled a list of 1200 drugs and other healing remedies used in the kingdom of the Aztecs. Beside priests, fortune tellers and sorcerers they also had pharmacists and doctors who for the most part healed with herbal remedies.

From *China*, several important herbal volumes have been recovered, among them the famous medicinal work *Pen Tsao Kang Mu* with its wonderful, very detailed illustrations of each particular plant.[3] As far back as 2000 years before Christ, Chinese doctors were using the plant "Ephedra sinica" for coughs and diseases of the lungs. Today many cough syrups contain ephedrine, exactly the same substance which is found in that plant. Probably the most popular of the traditional Chinese remedies was the Ginseng-root, which is taken today by the ton for impotence and fatigue. Scientific investigations have shown that the root, which resembles the wisened face of an old man, actually contains substances which have a mild stimulating effect.[4]

There would be much to write about plants and healing herbs in the ancient cultures of Babylon, Peru and India, of Greece and Rome. Buried under the dust of millenia there are hidden voluminous books full of strange mixtures and herbs magical chants, healing herbs the effects of which have been rediscovered and scientifically proved in our century.

In the *Bible*, we also find treatment with herbal remedies. In the second book of Kings 20:7 we read the prophet Isaiah's prescription for King Hezekiah: "Then Isaiah said, 'Prepare a poultice of figs.' They did so, and applied it to the boil, and he recovered."

During the Middle Ages the knowledge of herbal medicine was preserved by monks in Europe's monasteries. The famous herb-book of the monastery of St. Gall in Switzerland (written around 820 A.D.) starts with the words: "In the name of Christ lies the foundation for the art of healing."

Probably the best known physician of the Middle Ages was Theophrastus Bombastus von Hohenheim, also known as *Paracelsus* who lived from 1493 to 1541. In his person, Christian mysticism, Eastern natural philosophy and black magic joined hands. On the one hand he preached to his contemporaries: "The sick person who sets his hope in medicines is no Christian; but he who hopes in God, he truly is a Christian." [5] "But alongside this spirituality," writes the respected psycho-analyst C.G. Jung, "a countervailing spirit made itself felt to an almost frightening degree: there was no form of manticism and magic that Paracelsus did not practise himself or recommend to others."[6]

Although he speaks of God, "who has given strength and power to the plants to liberate man of his diseases so that he might not be overpowered by death prematurely," his true god is *Nature*, and his guides are demonic powers. [7] He even reproached the doctors of his time, claiming that they did not understand magic.

The works of Paracelsus have had a lasting influence on later generations of health practitioners, and his thoughts are still being considered as the foundation for the practice of holistic health in our day. The *tension between superficial religiosity and deep-seated occultism* has characterised many herbologists throughout the centuries right up to this day.

Herbs against cancer - medicine of today

Without herbal substances we could not have conceived modern medicine. Many medications, some of which one would never have thought of, are derived from plants. [8]

Did you know for instance that the most important drugs used in the treatment of *cancer* are herbal? The alkaloids vincristin and vinblastin are extracted from a Madagascan evergreen plant. With their help, dramatic successes have been achieved against Hodgkin's disease, acute lymphatic leukaemia, and Wilm's tumour (a rare kidney tumour in children). Where there was no hope only twenty years ago, patients today are experiencing remissions in 80 to 99 percent of the cases - thanks to herbal drugs.

Many herbal substances influence the *nervous system*. The most important pain relievers are derived from plants. Instead of *aspirin* one could take an extract of willow or poplar bark. Both contain the same substance, but the exact dosage of a tablet is easier and safer to determine. In addition the tablet contains a neutralising additive to prevent the salicylic acid from eroding the stomach's lining. We have already spoken of the importance of poppy derivates like *morphine* and related substances. Almost as important as the surgeon's scalpel is another herbal substance which is used in anaesthesia to relax the muscles: the Indian poison *curare*.

Plants are an invaluable asset in yet another area. Most people in the West today are dying of *cardio-vascular diseases*. Where would we be without the substance *digoxin* which is extracted from foxgloves? More than three million Americans are daily taking this drug to stay alive. Without digitalis and related compounds their heart could not cope with its task, and they would die prematurely from congestive cardiac failure.

Another killer-disease of our time, *hypertension* (high blood pressure), was initially treated with plant-derived drugs. Before 1950 the fate of patients with high blood pressure was sealed: strokes and heart and renal failure ensued. But then a substance was discovered in the plant Rauwolfia which enabled many patients with hypertension to lead a normal life. The plant had been known for thousands of years in the ayurvedic medicine of India where it was used for its calming effect.

There are many other diseases which doctors treat with herbal substances: *glaucoma*, for example, is treated with a substance extracted from a Nigerian bean. *Asthma* can be alleviated with ephedrine and theophylline, and mucus in the bronchial system is dissolved by using Ipecacuanha syrup.

Innumerable plants have a regulatory effect on the *digestive system:* some cause nausea, others resolve spasms; bananas induce constipation, whereas castor oil does the opposite. New emphasis has been put on bran and fibre since research reports indicated that intestinal cancer is much more common in populations living on a low-fibre diet.[9]

These few examples demonstrate that one cannot artificially dig a trench between medicine and therapy with effective herbal remedies. Where effects have been found, medicine makes use of naturally occurring substances. [10] However, many drugs which are found naturally in plants, can be reconstructed chemically and produced in their pure form. This has two distinct advantages:

1. The physician can determine the dosage more exactly. It is easier for the doctor to give two tablets of digoxin, the dose of which he knows exactly, than two drops of foxglove-tincture in which the amount of active ingredient is not determinable. The fine line between healing and poisoning can all too easily be crossed.

2. Poisonous substances occurring in the same plant are thus eliminated. It is not at all true, that "biological remedies" are always safe and without danger. Many plants contain highly poisonous substances which are only helpful when used in their proper concentration. [11]

The producers of natural remedies often claim that a remedy is only effective when given in its whole "natural form." In other words: Vitamin C in a capsule would not be as effective as the same vitamin in an orange. Whereas it certainly is true that a fresh orange is much more enjoyable than a tablet, this contention cannot be verified by objective research.

What is herbal medicine?

Herbal Medicine (or phytotherapy, as it is sometimes called) is based on the belief that nature provides the best remedies for most diseases. Actually, this is not so far from the truth. I consider it one of the major merits of herbal practitioners that they have sown a healthy distrust in the chemical medicine of our times.

However, the emphasis on chemicals is not only the doctors' fault. Many people do not want to change their life style. They would rather continue their unhealthy diet and take a handful of vitamin and mineral supplements every day. They are not really interested in facing and solving the problems which deprive them of their sleep. It is easier to swallow tranquillizers and amphetamines. Considering the number of "prescription-junkies" one understands the outcry against chemistry, and the counter-movement back to less dangerous and addictive remedies such as the herbal tinctures of the ancestors.

However positive the intentions of herbal medicine are, one still has to maintain a healthy scepticism. Quackery and occult practices are rampant and have made it difficult to discern where help for the body ends and harm to the soul begins.

But again, it would be wrong to overgeneralise: the following are three examples among the variety of herbal healers:

1. A herbologist who refuses to apply occult methods to his art.

2. The group whose remedies are produced on the basis of an obviously occult philosophy, namely Anthroposophy.

3. Practitioners who use psychic powers to arrive at a diagnosis and treatment.

Traditional herbal medicine

During the course of my research I have made the acquaintance of men and women whose genuine concern is to help their patients regain a healthier life style. They have invested their whole life into that one goal. They are not trying to start a new diet fad or herbal cult, and they clearly stay away from occult methods, carefully choosing the plants they prefer in therapy.

One of these herbal practitioners is Mr. Vogel who received an honorary doctorate from a Californian osteopathic college for his research on plants. His book *The Little Doctor*[12] has sold more than half a million copies world wide. Thousands of families from the Finnish north to the lone farms of Australia consult this book when they become sick. The 860-page volume is a colourful collection of more or less helpful advice. Whereas the critical scientist would find many things he would probably doubt, the book certainly has helped many families save a trip to the doctor for a minor ailment. Many people would do well to follow Vogel's advice concerning a healthy life-style.

"Bioforce Inc." produces the remedies that Mr. Vogel recommends. One sunny afternoon the director of production took a whole hour to show me around the facilities. Apart from the fact that the basic substances in the medicines are plant extracts, the production and packing did not differ from any other pharmaceutical plant. Certainly it had nothing in common with a dimly lit sorcerer's kitchen with a huge cauldron over the hearth, where some people would imagine herbal remedies are brewed.

Later, I had the opportunity to get together personally with the stocky, vigorous natural doctor when he gave a lecture at Konstanz University. In the course of our conversation I asked him some questions:

How does Mr. Vogel find a new herbal remedy? He has dedicated a whole chapter of his book to this question. [13] If he has the impression that a plant may have a useful effect, he tries it on himself - unless it is poisonous. To prevent other nutrients from disturbing the impact of the herb on his body, he fasts for 2 - 3 days prior to the experiment. "Depending on what herb we ingest," he writes, "we will experience an activation of our intestines or the function of our kidneys. It may exert an influence on our stomach and increase our appetite, or revitalise another bodily function. When you have a well-functioning body, you can easily perceive certain effects. This is the so-called proving of a remedy in the healthy subject."

For the scientifically trained physician these explanations are largely inadequate, as we know how differently individual patients can react to the same remedy. Moreover, certain herbal substances, such as digoxin, do not display their effect on the healthy, but only on the failing heart. But at least it is to Vogel's credit that he does not employ occult methods in his search for new remedies.

This leads us to the next question: *What is his opinion of the occult techniques many of his colleagues work with?* In a letter to one of his patients who asked him the same question, the herbalist, who is an active member of the

Jehovah's Witnesses, writes:

> Let me tell you honestly and frankly that I
> am opposed to the use of radiesthesia... In
> Bioforce Inc. there is nothing that has to do
> with occult practices, as I am strongly
> opposed to these dark machinations. I
> have seen enough occultism among
> Indians and other primitive tribes, and
> know that it is inspired by Satan and that
> he wants to bring people under his
> bondage.

In another letter he says:

> There are many health practitioners who
> are dabbling in the occult. I have protested
> against this in the Association of Natural
> Healers and told them I will not tolerate
> any discussion of occult methods in our
> meetings. One can be a natural healer and
> still work on a serious, correct scientific
> basis.

It is obvious that Vogel won many enemies by his straight talking.

Despite the clear stand Vogel takes in his letters, there are two criticisms one cannot easily dismiss:

1. Vogel repeatedly serves as a lecturer in congresses where, among other methods, acupuncture, Yoga, Eastern meditation and Anthroposophy are propagated. Thus, despite verbal affirmations, he is nonetheless unequally yoked with people who promote Eastern-occult techniques and teachings.

2. He prescribes remedies and gives medical advice to patients he has never personally examined and whose history he knows only insufficiently. I know about the case of a 78-year-old patient with skin cancer, asthma and heart

118 Healing at any Price?

failure who, in addition, developed a very painful Herpes zoster (shingles). Without her knowledge her neighbour asked Mr. Vogel what to do about the excruciating pain and the asthma. A few days later a letter arrived with the recommendation of light diet, kidney drops, asthma drops, calcium tablets and three homoeopathic remedies (one in the potency of 12X). He asked no further questions, but added a sentence on the nature of the ailment, which in the variety of its possible meaning could have been interpreted in many ways.

Dr. H.C. Vogel is an example of a herbal practitioner who openly rejects occult methods, but who is not always successful in everyday practice, in drawing a clear line between a serious, scientific herbal medicine, and the questionable activities of many of his colleagues.

Anthroposophical medicine: herbs with cosmic power

Let us now go one step further to remedies which are obviously and wilfully based on a foundation of magic. [14] The writings of Carlos Castaneda and Eileen Caddy of the Scottish Findhorn Community, both of whom claim to be inspired by "spirit guides", bear witness to the fact that herbalism and sorcery is being widely publicised. Some of the better known herbal remedies, especially in Europe, are produced on the principles of Anthroposophy, another occult philosophy. [15, 16] Its founder, Rudolf Steiner, (1861-1925) discovered at the age of eight that he had the gift of clairvoyance. This brought him into contact with familiar spirits which gave him his first insights into the transcendental world. But there was no one he could talk to about his experiences. One day, he met a cantankerous old herbalist who further led him into the world of mysticism and the occult. Another person whom he called his "spiritual master" gave him the goal which he was to pursue throughout his life: "To integrate science and religion; to introduce God into science and nature into religion."[17]

Around the turn of the century he became the general

secretary of the *Theosophical Society* which contributed considerably to the Eastern elements in his teachings. Although he later left the movement, *Karma* and *reincarnation* remained pivotal in his "anthroposophical" teaching. Thus, his "Waldorf education",[18] practised in over a hundred institutions all over the world, is based on the notion that "fate (or karma) has led immature souls into sick or deformed bodies." It is the objective of this special education "to allow them to develop new strength for their next incarnation."[19]

Steiner even founded a new church with a doctrinally twisted concept of Christ. He sees the reason for Christ's death on the cross to be His betrayal of ancient mysteries for which He was subsequently punished. Harmony with God is attained by meditation for the purpose of training the person's spiritual consciousness.[20]

In his incessant creative urge, Steiner wrote more than 100 books and gave more than 1000 lectures. Rudolf Steiner not only gave guidelines for special education, teaching, art, music, agriculture, theology and philosophy, but also for medicine. The basic textbook of anthroposophic healing is entitled *Spiritual Science and Medicine*,[21] in which Steiner introduces a completely new concept of man.

It is so completely different from scientific medicine that it is extremely difficult to grasp the anthroposophical theories. Steiner based his medical views on *astrology* and his own "enlightenment through spiritual science" which he claims to have received while meditating. His teachings are electic, combining elements from all major occult philosophies.

In a similar way to Chinese philosophy, Steiner constructs relationships between body and universe, and between metals and remedies. How those connections are derived, remains unclear to the outsider. The following excerpt may however illustrate the vivid fantasy with which metals are related to planets, healing forces, spirits, Greek mythologies and scientific insights of the beginning of the 20th century. Excerpts that only an anthrosophical believer could really understand.

The substances, vitalised through the silver process, have to be subordinated to the whole organism and should not receive any individual life. They have to be guided to a higher function, a process which is facilitated through Mercurius. Since ancient times, Mercurius was regarded as the author of negotiating and connecting powers. Mercurius, the envoy of the gods, is mediating between heaven and earth, between higher spiritual beings and man, as well as in different areas. Here we have a primal healing principle, that many diseases are the result of a lack in mediation: and where there is too much, substantially or processually, in one place, there is a deficiency in another. This leads to accumulations which are dissolved by a Mercurian process... In a higher sense this is in fact a healing activity, and the reason for the choice of Mercurius as the god of the physicians. The powers of Mercurius are created in the lungs. They mediate, through inspiration and expiration, the vitalising and mortifying energies. With this typical human-animalistic respiratory process we have the foundation for the higher life of the soul which reaches far beyond the biological plane of life.[22]

This quotation demonstrates that the effect of anthroposophical remedies is not simply expected on a chemical level in the body. Rudolf Steiner is rather convinced that his herbal remedies would unfold the same creative powers in the microcosm of the human body, as do the "macrocosmic planetary-ethereal processes in the creation of the world."[23] As a consequence the plants that are used for the anthroposophical remedies are planted, harvested and processed at certain hours when the Zodiac influences them in a special way. Through ritual movements and rhythmic temperature changes, the remedies are supposed to attract cosmic powers. Very often the herbal tinctures are processed according to homoeopathic principles, which the Steiner disciples believe they can use to facilitate the transference of "vital energy" to their products.[24]

The remedies of the San Diego based "Medicine Wheel" are prepared in a very similar way. In their catalogue[25] they write: "As much as possible, we follow the lunar cycle and use the power of prayer to bring forth the spirit of the herbs." Their symbol, "The Medicine Shield", is described as follows:

> The shield on our tincture labels shows the tree of life, ever reaching upwards. The spirit in the tree represents the Hopi symbol for the Great Spirit - our Creator. The bear is Eskimo and is the sign of the West, symbolising humankind's earthly roots and looking within; while the bird of the East... represents spiritual humanity and the heights to which we can soar. The sun represents the dawning of the new age and the rebirth of an illuminated human being... The seven feathers hanging from the shield are the seven levels of consciousness, or bodily chakras, that humanity must rise through to achieve wholeness on the earth. Explanations aside, the shield is a mandala for personal contemplation.
>
> The Medicine Wheel is the complete circle, or wholeness of spiritual understanding, knowledge and expression, that all people are striving to attain.

Flower remedies

Similar beliefs are held by the various groups that are

working with Flower remedies. Mrs. Bellhouse, for instance, the founder of *Vita Florum,* believes that she is led to the proper flowers by "Divine guidance."[26] She then holds the flowers "in water, in sunlight, until their power passes into it." Among other effects, "Vita Florum" remedies are supposed to "help in positively directing our inner-consciousness into calm, unitive, constructive states of being and awareness, so that our other-consciousness can contribute peace and harmony to our physical selves."

Another flower-remedy, *Exultation of Flowers*[27], is described as consisting of the potencies of many flowers which are harvested at "an ideal time when the transference may be effected... sometimes around the time of the full moon." The flower radiations are then transferred to water and sold in small bottles. They are supposed to operate "on the radiations flowing through the human body." However, in 1961, a British Court ordered that all bottles be labelled as "containing one hundred percent water, since the radiations cannot be identified by chemical analysis."

By far the best known in this group are the *Bach Flower Remedies.*[28] Developed by a homoeopathic physician in the early years of our century they are supposed to "restore peace of mind and hope to the sick." Thus he prepared thirty-eight remedies to treat the following conditions:

1. Fear
2. Uncertainty
3. Insufficient interest in present circumstances.
4. Loneliness
5. Oversensitivity to influences and ideas.
6. Despondency or despair
7. Over-care for welfare of others.

His followers affirm that these remedies "are not homoeopathic, nor do they have different potencies, for *the power set free from the flowers is the unalterable life-force itself"*.

Bach's Flower Remedies are a glaring example of the fact that many herbalists are not only operating on dubious cosmic forces but that they are thwarting the goal they have set for themselves: to treat man as a whole. The only benefit offered by these remedies is that they replace more dangerous chemical agents. But they fail to deal with man's psychological and spiritual needs, which can only be fully met by a changed life that is founded in Jesus Christ.

Prescription with pendulum and magic

The celebrated French herbalist *Maurice Messegue* was one day called to the bed of the president of the radical social party in France. The elderly overweight politician had been suffering from arthritis for years and none of his doctors were able to help him. He therefore turned to a natural healer.

Messegue reached into his pocket, took out a pendulum and let it swing over the patient. With the other hand he took little flasks out of his waistcoat pocket. While the patient's friends were still wondering what he was doing, he concluded the examination.

"Tomorrow I'll bring you a little bottle with an essence," he told the party-president.

"Why can't you give me that miraculous potion right away?"

"Mon president, I first have to prepare it especially for you."

"Are you giving all arthritis-patients the same?"

"No Sir. While I had the pendulum swing over you, I have simultaneously tested, with the help of these test tubes, the herbs that will help you."[29]

This little story illustrates how many naturopaths, chiropractors, and psychic healers arrive at their diagnosis and their therapy. Instead of objective tests they prefer to use psychic means, especially the pendulum and radionic devices, pulse-diagnosis or altered states of consciousness.

Many of these practitioners have a *religious veneer:* Messegue confesses to be a practicing Catholic. The famous Abbe Mermet and Swiss Abbe Kuenzle were Catholic priests. Psychic healer Norman Shealy, M.D. practises in a Catholic hospital in Springfield, Missouri. Other occult working naturopaths come from a Protestant background such as the Lutheran pastor, Bolte. Even among evangelical

Christians there is a pervasive uncertainty in the evaluation of psychic methods. Dr. Kurt Koch writes:

> I have met doctors, pastors, missionaries, and even evangelists who use the rod or pendulum and believe they have received this gift from God. Satan's cunning is very evident when even believing Christians are deceived by him.[30]

A Christian vocabulary is no quality guarantee for a holistic practitioner.

As we have seen in the previous chapter, radiesthesia is an occult method based on the same Eastern-occult assumptions as other related practices, Here again, it is assumed that every person and every object has its individual radiation which is not measurable with instruments but by psychic sensitivity. Let me concentrate here only on the use of the pendulum in the diagnosis and treatment of herbal practitioners. The pendulum is supposed to pick up the slightest change in a patient's energy balance. Thus history taking and lab testing become unnecessary. Occult herbalists find out the diagnosis simply by consulting their pendulum or using other psychic means.

Having read the book to this point, you will anticipate the Eastern principle of treatment: the energetic balance has to be restored. Austrian new age physicist Maresch believes that every plant has its own "specific microwave radiation."[31] The pendulum is supposed to indicate the substance most likely to counteract the energy deficit of the patient. [32]

While the healer touches the patient or an object belonging to the patient he literally asks the pendulum some questions. One dowsing herbalist writes: "I ask my pendulum, 'Is the appropriate remedy Ammonium phosphoricum? If it responds with 'No,' I try the next product until I have found the right one, and the pendulum answers with 'Yes'."[33]

This question-answer ritual makes nonsense of some

herbologists' assertions that they measure radiation. Let me reiterate that the use of radiesthesia is a *form of divination* and can bring a patient under occult oppression.

How can you avoid occult practitioners?

There is no doubt that many herbs have a genuine healing effect. God has given them to us to alleviate and cure a host of ailments. Thus, whilst I am warning against the majority of herbal practitioners I do not want to throw the baby out with the bath water. Speaking up against the Mormons does not mean we reject dark suits, ties and bikes. In the same way, we cannot condemn the use of herbal remedies only because they are often prescribed by occult practitioners. We need to find the balance that was outlined by Paul in regard to the meat offered to idols (see page 172 in chapter 12).

How then, are we to use herbal remedies without getting in touch with occult practices?

1. Purchase a book describing the most important applications of plants, herbal teas and poultices.[34] Avoid books that contain references to radiations, energies and psychic healing, or recommend, besides unquestionably good material, magic formulae and rituals for the healing of various diseases. Moreover, every pharmacist will gladly give you information on which teas to use in certain situations.

2. Before starting a prolonged treatment with herbal remedies, consult your family physician to exclude a more serious disease. All too often the application of herbal remedies has allowed a tumour to grow to an extent where surgical removal was no longer possible.[35]

3. Avoid every practitioner or physician who does not take a clear stand against occult practices such as radiesthesia, magic formulae, palmistry, magnetism and healing at a distance by "mental broadcast." Do not consult any healer or physician who offers you yoga, Zen and

Eastern forms of meditation to solve your problems.

4. When you are buying natural remedies and herbal products, confine yourself to brands which are free of Eastern-occult overtones.

5. *Most important:* Trust God for your healing (inward or outward) and not the goddess "Nature." Praise Him for the herbs He created. And when you tell your friends of the success of your herbal treatment, give the Creator the honour He deserves.

Ten

Mysterious Phenomena: is there an Explanation?

What is actually happening when a patient is freed from his pain through the treatment of a naturopath? How can homoeopathy help when there is actually no active substance in the potentiated remedy? What is it that makes reflexology alleviate back-aches and brighten up depression? Why do people sleep better and with less pain after they have a radionic device installed under their bed? Why is it that herbalists succeed in cases where doctors have laboured for years without results?

Many Christians, when asked for an explanation of unconventional cures, are inclined to assume immediately that occult powers were involved. In my view, such a knock-out punch is too simplistic. There seem to be five possible explanations for these puzzling healing phenomena:

1. The person would have regained his health with or without any particular therapy.
2. The healers, with their remedies and therapies, trigger an actual though not yet fully understood effect, e.g.via the nervous system or intrinsic biochemical agents.
3. The cure is a result of a placebo effect.
4.Suggestion or hypnosis are somehow involved in the healing.
5. The patient is healed through the direct influence of demonic powers.

The healing potential of the body

The most important assistant of physicians as well as "holistic" therapists is the so called phenomenon of "spontaneous healing". What do we mean by this expression?

With the help of its wonderful God-given immune system the body is often capable of more or less healing itself. Even cancer-cells can be held in check by the healthy body for a long time, until their growth finally becomes overwhelming.

A common cold heals by itself whether or not there is any medical intervention. Nonetheless a young woman excitedly told me about the wonderful effects of reflexology on her cold: "Can you imagine, it was completely gone after only three days!" The glory and her money she gave to the healer, not considering that it was God who had equipped her body with the means to overcome her sickness.

Warts are another example. A man told me about his wife who had suffered from extremely painful warts on the soles of her feet. Finally a surgeon removed them, but one year later they came back as painful as before. After months of indecision the woman finally gave in to her husband's urging and underwent homoeopathic treatment. The months went by, the lady faithfully took the remedies, and nothing happened. "But after five months," he excitedly explained to me, "my wife suddenly felt no more pain, and within a few more months the warts had disappeared. Isn't this proof of the effectiveness of homoeopathy?"

Not really. Warts are caused by a virus, and are usually conquered by the body's own immune system, after a long battle. "Warts have a high spontaneous healing rate," writes respected dermatologist, Professor Steigleder, "but healing can be protracted for years. Sudden cures have led to the assumption that magic procedures may indeed be curative. However, this has been contradicted in a controlled study."[1] Nevertheless, because the last attempt to treat his wife had been homoeopathy, this gentleman gave all honour to the homoeopathic physician. Yet - who created the body's immune system?

The physician is only God's assistant

When there is a fracture, the doctor can set the broken

bone and put it in a cast. Yet only a few hours after the accident an amazing process is taking place: white cells carried by the blood-stream start to clean up the damaged tissue. Then new cells begin to grow. The blood brings nutritients and calcium and soon a firm "bridge" spans the gap. A few weeks later the cast can be removed, and the leg or arm is as strong as ever!

Now, did the doctor heal the leg? Of course not! It was the wonderful God-created mechanism that led to the healing of the fractured limb. The physician was only an assistant.

Even when a surgeon removes a cancerous tumour, he cannot claim the praise for the healing all for himself. Without the amazing God-given repair teams in blood and tissues all his efforts would have been in vain.

Unknown mechanisms

But aren't there perhaps other healing mechanisms we simply have not discovered yet? Are psychic healers ahead of their time just as the discoverers of bacteria were ahead of theirs? Is there perhaps, hidden underneath holistic therapy, an actual healing process which will some day be discovered through new research?

At least for the alleviation of pain through electro-acupuncture in anaesthesia there appears to be some demonstrable effect. I have discussed some of the theories in chapter 4. However, if acupuncture-analgesia really does have some scientific validity, it excludes ninety percent of the characteristics ancient Chinese scholars and modern acupuncturists attribute to it.

What is left is a system of electrical skin and muscle stimulation to support anaesthesia. The only thing it has in common with acupuncture is its name. The world-soul "Tao", the cosmic energy "Ch'i", the polar forces "Yin" and "Yang", the "harmony with the universe" - all these concepts have to be abandoned. It does not even need the meridian system or an exact placement of the needles at the traditional sites to achieve pain relief, which, in addition, is very variable from one patient to the next.

But patients, in their search for healing, are seeking "magical", mysterious new forms of healing. This is a major part of acupuncture's appeal. Therefore, its practitioners will not go along with the scientific reduction of their art. *Logically explainable methods lose their fascination.*

Already hospitals are abandoning acupuncture as impractical and unsafe compared with techniques which are more reliable and easier to handle. The country that originally triggered the acupuncture-boom is moving away from it. Today only one or two out of twenty patients in the People's Republic of China are being anaesthetised with the help of acupuncture. They increasingly depend on Western medicine instead.

The amazing network

But what about the results of acupuncture in the actual cure of diseases? Is there possibly a genuine effect? Is it really possible that the massage of foot zones promotes better blood circulation in the brain? In order to answer these questions, let's take a look at the wonderfully designed *autonomic nervous system*. Every person has two nervous systems: the *central* (or voluntary) and the *autonomic* (or involuntary, vegetative) nervous system. If I see a beautiful red apple hanging on a tree and reach out to pick it, I am using my voluntary or central nervous system: as my brain receives the visual stimuli, my pleasure centre is activated. Now I command my arm to move and my fingers to open in order to grasp the apple at just the right time. Even if this all happens within a split-second, I am still controlling every movement with my will.

But there is a second system in the body beyond conscious control. Consisting of a network of nerve fibres, it follows every blood vessel and surrounds every gland and inner organ with a fine-spun cocoon. This system is called the vegetative or autonomic nervous system, and it is beyond the control of will-power.

For example, when I step out of a dark room into bright sunlight, my pupils constrict in a split-second whether I want them to or not. If you take a bike tour in warm weather you will automatically start to perspire. The perspiration evaporates thus keeping the body at an extraordinarily constant temperature.

When our intestinal system receives food to digest, the autonomic system orders tiny muscular flood-gates in the blood vessels to open up. The increased supply of blood will then transport away the digested nutritients without any conscious action on our part. The same process takes place in the brain for example, when we need extra energy to solve a difficult mathematical problem.

If the function of the autonomic nervous system, with its sympathetic and parasympathetic components, is disturbed, all sorts of illnesses can arise: duodenal ulcers, asthma, diarrhoea, constipation, rashes, menstrual difficulties, impotence, hypertension, heart-rhythm abnormalities, tension headaches, migraine, and many more. Obviously each one of these diseases could have other causes, but very often there is some connection with the autonomic nervous system.

Duodenal ulcers and the psyche

These correlations are supported by research, especially in the study of duodenal ulcers. Closely packed together, the stomach's lining of mucous membrane contains innumerable tiny glands. They produce the enzymes and gastric acid necessary for digestion. At each of those millions of tiny glands there ends a silken fibre from the autonomic nervous system.

We only have to see a juicy, fresh-baked chicken on a plate, and the saliva will begin to flow into our mouth, while stomach glands start producing more acid in order to be able to digest the anticipated tasty bite.

Stress, anxiety, anger, worry and guilt can all disrupt the autonomic system's usual rhythm. This stimulates the gastric glands to produce excessive acid for too long a period of time. The acid then flows into the duodenum, where it corrodes the lining of the duodenum and an ulcer is the result. Piercing pain, malaise and loss of appetite follow.

Modern medicine has already developed a whole array of weapons against this so-called "executive's syndrome". The first step is an attempt to neutralise the acid with regular small meals. Then there are antacids to chew, aluminium and magnesium containing medicines to drink, or expensive "Tagamet" tablets to take. If these fail, surgery may be necessary to sever the nerve that causes the overstimulation of acid production or even to remove the lower part of the stomach.

Wouldn't it be wonderful if we were able to influence these nerves by a conscious effort of the will instead of having to resort to such drastic cures? It would be fantastic if we could simply give them the command not to produce so much gastric acid! But this is not possible directly. Obviously an executive could take a real holiday and hide away in a quiet mountain chalet. Then his nervous system would probably quieten down, and the ulcers would heal. But it isn't all that simple! His family still has to survive. Also it's not easy for a highly-strung person, living under constant tension, suddenly to become the relaxed easy-going type.

There are, however, ways to outwit the vegetative nervous system and to change its function permanently. How is that possible? The path leads from a surprising discovery to a completely new understanding of natural healing.

The placebo-phenomenon

Some time ago two patients suffering from headache were given the same tablets with the comment that it was a new, promising drug. The first patient was told that the pill would alleviate her headache and give her new vigour. The second lady was warned that the tablet was still in its experimental phase and could possibly cause some unpleasant side-effects; but it was worth trying nevertheless.

By the next day both patients experienced the symptoms that had been predicted. The first patient felt much better, the other complained of a tingling sensation in the fingertips and slight heart-burn. Yet both had received the same medicine! How was it possible that there was such a difference?

Both ladies had been given a "placebo", a tablet with no active ingredients except lactose, a form of sugar. Their reactions demonstrated that the effect of a tablet is only partly caused by the chemical ingredient. Much more important are the patient's expectations of the drug.

The word "placebo" comes from the Latin, meaning "I will please". In the middle-ages the word was used to describe a fawning hypocrite, a flattering courtier. Modern medicine adopted the term to define a medication the physician prescribes only to please his patient, but which contains no actual ingredients.

But even so, "placebos" have such an amazing success that at a medical convention, a well-known expert declared: "A placebo is a drug."[2]

What are the diseases that can be treated with placebos? Surprisingly, the list is practically the same as the catalogue of ailments which can be improved or healed through natural methods.[3] Improvement through placebo therapy is seen in the following problems:

-pain conditions of various origin	in 28% of the cases
-headaches	in 62
-migraine	in 32
-colds	in 45
-neuroses	in 34
-angina pectoris	in 18
-digestive-tract complaints	in 58
-arthritic pain	in 49
-menstrual discomfort	in 24

On the average, approximately 30 to 40 percent of all patients respond to placebos very well, while another third does not experience any improvement at all. People who respond well to fake medications are called "placebo-responders". It is more than coincidence that about the same percentage of patients, one third, show excellent results with the application of acupuncture, homoeopathy, herbal remedies and other unconventional treatments.

"You are my last hope!"

Scientists have found that the most important factor in the prescription of placebos is the relationship between physician and patient. "The more impressive and charming the personality of a physician is, the less suited he is to experiment objectively with new drugs. His personality will influence the reaction of the test-person and bias the results."[4]

In one experiment, a new tranquillizer was prescribed by two different doctors.

> The results showed that those patients experienced the best effect whose doctor was enthusiastic about the new tranquillizer. He was interested in his patients, and they had confidence in him. He was friendly, did a thorough physical examination, showed self-confidence and competence. He was without contradictions. This human attitude was totally convincing - and therefore an ideal prerequisite for a positive placebo reaction.
>
> The second group, treated by a therapeutic nihilist, reacted very unsatisfactorily to the same drug. This physician was preoccupied with his personal problems, aloof, irritable, moody. He was unable to convince the patients that they could expect anything positive from the drug: his success was accordingly poor.[5]

Placebos are especially effective when patients are in extreme need and will swallow anything that could possibly help. This is exactly the situation most patients are in when they consult a health practitioner. The patients often comment: "You are my last hope!" Then it doesn't matter what the healer does: whether he inserts needles or prescribes a herbal tincture - the patient believes, and is willing to follow every advice.

Something interesting is happening, at this point, in the brain. As new research has revealed, the brain-cells produce a substance, called "endorphin", which has similar qualities to morphine. Endorphins have a marked pain-reducing and tranquillizing effect, and could well serve as the explanation for the wonderful results of placebos and natural healing methods.[6]

Could the endorphins serve to measure believing confidence scientifically? An answer is not possible, at this point. One thing is sure, however; *faith* in the effectiveness of a medicine causes a change in the reactions of the autonomic nervous system. The blood-vessels in the brain relax, and the migraine disappears. The acid-production in the stomach-lining decreases, and the ulcers heal.

The healing power of suggestion

If faith is such a strong factor in changing a person's condition, shouldn't it be possible to heal diseases merely through the power of the spoken word? In the case of psychosomatic diseases, experience indicates that suggestive methods do play a major role in the healing process.

French pharmacologist, Coué, recommended that his patients use his method of *self-hypnosis*, or *"auto-suggestion"*. Thousands of patients streamed to him with ailments ranging from insomnia to hemiplegia, due to a cerebral stroke. In a large auditorium, Coué held daily lectures to teach his patients the techniques of auto-suggestion. After a few experiments which demonstrated the power of suggestion, he asked all participants to close their eyes. Then he gave every person according to their particular ailment a formula to memorise and instructed them to repeat it 20-30 times a day.

Every morning, immediately after

> awakening; every evening, just before
> falling asleep - close your eyes and
> whisper, barely loud enough to hear your
> own voice, about 20 times the following
> formula:... 'In every respect I am getting
> better and better every day.'[7]

Coué's method of self-hypnosis had unbelievable success, but the dangers are apparent. The formulas the patients were told to repeat over and over again in their morning-meditation were very similar to Hindu-mantras. Through their monotonous rhythm they were producing a form of trance, thereby opening up the spirit for potential influences beyond human control.

The question arises whether similar mechanisms are operating in the ministry of charismatic healers as well. As the meeting approaches its climax, and the Hallelujahs get louder and louder, and the prayers more and more fervent, the atmosphere becomes highly conducive to healing through *mass-suggestion*. Sometimes, at Kathryn Kullman's direction hundred of patients would stand and wave the arms they had not previously been able to move because of arthritic pain. And many people really believed they were healed. An experienced surgeon[8] later followed up a large number of patients and found that many among those who were "healed" did feel better for a while, but died from the same disease they had before the "miracle". Permanent healings were frequently reported only by those patients who had been suffering from psycho-somatic illnesses.

I do not want to deny that perhaps there were genuine healings, and I am sure that many people went home positively changed inwardly and outwardly. Nevertheless, we have to be careful with overly enthusiastic reports.

The great success of all kinds of healers can be explained, to a large extent, by the fact that over 50 percent of all diseases a physician encounters in his office are of a psycho-somatic nature. But the doctor's problem is that he has much too little time to listen to his patients in order to help them. Patients are disappointed or even furious when their doctor tells them: "There is nothing seriously wrong with your back." As a consequence their suffering seems to increase, and they become more open to the healing power of suggestion.

Comprehensive studies have demonstrated that "there is no organic function in the human body which cannot be influenced by suggestion."[9]

Unfortunately healing is not the only thing that can be facilitated through suggestion. Severe damage, without an apparent external cause, can be brought about as well. Through persuasion alone researchers were able to produce allergic skin rashes.[10] In another patient they succeeded in producing a burn blister just through the guided imagery of laying a searingly hot coin on her skin.[11] Similar phenomena, whether good or bad, can be produced through "autogenic training", hypnosis or bio-feedback.[12] All these methods tend to make body and spirit highly susceptible to influences beyond conscious control.

Faith - the magic key

The key-factor in all these forms of suggestion is *faith*. Let me go one step further: it is important to *open your spirit* for mind-controlling influences beyond yourself. Auto-suggestion, hypnosis and some aspects of bio-feedback have such a close spiritual affinity to Eastern-mystical meditation that Christians should wonder: What am I actually opening myself up to? Who do I really believe?

It is not insignificant that the Bible places so much emphasis on *faith* because it is a mighty bridge to the unseen world of the supernatural. Faith can bring us into a relationship with God, but faith can also establish contact with dark, demonic entities.

Claude M. Bristol writes in his book *The Magic of Believing:*

> I have read literally thousands of books on modern psychology, metaphysics, ancient magic, Voodooism, Yogism, Theosophy, Christian Science... and many others dealing with what I call 'mind

> stuff', as well as the philosophies and
> teachings of the great masters of the past.
>
> Gradually I discovered that there is a
> golden thread that runs through all the
> teachings and makes them work for those
> who sincerely accept and apply them, and
> that thread can be named in the single
> word - *belief*.[13]

The same applies to healing through practitioners who
claim to control certain cosmic powers through meditation.
"The patients who consult them are aware of the healers'
lack of medical knowledge, but they go because they
believe that there are certain people endowed with
transcendental powers," writes respected professor of
psychosomatics, Arthur Jores.[14]

He continues with the statement that there is practically
no difference between the activity of a psychic healer and
that of a primitive witch-doctor:

> In both cases, everything depends on
> the faith of the patient and his greatest
> possible submission to the particular
> method. The more intensive the surrender,
> the more sudden is the healing. These
> then, are the miracles taking place so often
> in the offices of quacks and fringe-
> therapists, and which occur so rarely in
> our hospitals. One can really talk about the
> *power of faith*...
>
> There is no difference, whether it is
> faith in a new healing remedy, in the
> supernatural power of the healer, or in
> God. If we consider what this attitude of
> faith entails, we can describe it as
> submission to a higher will. Faith means
> renunciation of one's own ego, of all the
> entanglements most people live in...

And Professor Jores dares not exclude the possibility that

there is more to this attitude of faith: "a direct influence of unconscious mind to unconscious mind, of spirit to spirit..."

Do not believe every spirit

The Bible warns us of blind faith in anything. "Why not if it helps?" many would say. Read the comments of the apostle John: "Dear friends, do not believe every spirit, but test the spirits to see whether they are from God, because many false prophets have gone out into the world."[15] We cannot be indifferent to whom we give our faith, or to whom we submit our spirit.

For Christians, there is a fundamental difference between faith in Christ Jesus and faith in cosmic powers or quacks. When Jesus says, "Take heart daughter, your faith has healed you,"[16] He means something entirely different from the faith required of Lao-Tse's disciples when they wanted their remedies and life-elixirs to work (see page 30).

Uncritical faith in spiritual powers opens the doors of our minds. Parapsychology-professor Hans Bender writes: "A patient's anxious fear, his emotional bond and believing submission to the person from whom the healing or improvement is expected, create favourable conditions for the occurrence of psychic phenomena."[17]

But faith is no guarantee that experiences of supernatural phenomena will always turn out positive. Although Transcendental Meditation promises "perfect health", some meditators have had such anxiety-provoking encounters that they had to be admitted to psychiatric hospitals. Yogis warn that evil powers can take control over the spirit when a person is open to them.[18] Similarly, one should be careful not to give oneself over to "magnetic" or "cosmic" powers, even when they are camouflaged by scientific "research" or "proof", or - worse still - by a religious veneer.

Neutral powers?

Parapsychologists are studiously trying to verify the occult aspects of unconventional medicine with the help of complicated and esoteric theories. People who do not want to believe in supernatural powers are groping for models that can explain how a cure can "function", when there is no chemical, anatomical, or psychological explanation. Yet it proves extremely difficult to keep psychic and occult powers apart.

Do telepathy, clairvoyance, radiesthesia and magnetism form part of man's God-given potential that not everybody knows how to use? Is healing only from the occult when there is a tangible encounter with demonic entities, or when witchcraft and magic are undoubtedly being practised?

Does a patient have to have a satanic mass read for his recovery in order to get entangled in occult bondage? Or does it suffice to surrender to a health practitioner who relies on unmeasurable energies, invisible meridians, or cosmic potentials? To what extent is healing by holistic methods psychological only, and to what extent is it occult?

According to J. Stafford Wright:

> It is impossible to draw a hard and fast boundary between occult and psychic powers, because the occult can include the psychic. When there is contact with spirits, they will make use of the slumbering human potential. Thus, there are persons using their own latent human powers, who at the same time are instruments of spirits who use these abilities.[19]

So, even experienced counsellors find it hard to draw the line. Let's face some hard questions: Are the energies used in acupuncture really neutral? Are the radionic forces a dowser claims to feel really mere natural vibrations, as yet undetected by scientific research? Are "magnetic" radiations really God-given gifts for the healing of the afflicted? And should we make it our goal to develop our hidden psychic potential? Why is it that those "Christians" who develop psychic abilities, are so inclined towards magic and Eastern mysticism? Why is it that they make humanism their creed instead of accepting the sovereignty of God? Why is it that they advocate subtle Christians forms of monism, watering down the Holy Spirit to a mere healing force?

Brooks Alexander, director of the Spiritual Counterfeits Project in Berkeley, California, says in an essay:

> It is not difficult to see that such psychic manipulation could turn an otherwise benign form of treatment into a spiritual booby trap. The nature of the doctor-patient relationship implicitly involves a kind of trust in and submission to the healer on many levels. For a Christian to accept the passive stance of "patient" before a practitioner who exercises spiritual power (either in his own right or as a channel for other influences) could easily result in spiritual derangement or bondage.
>
> It is probable that none of the Eastern or occult healing techniques are 'neutral' in themselves, even when ostensibly divorced from overt philosophical statements; the metaphysical framework from which they emerge is so pervasive and encompassing that every detail of practice is intricately related to elements of the underlying belief system.[20]

Thus, if we want to evaluate the spiritual powers behind holistic health methods, we must take a closer look at their effects on the faith of health practitioners and their patients. Truth cannot contradict itself. Supernatural healing powers, if inspired by God, cannot contradict God's Word in their underlying assumptions.

What then is the message of the Holistic Health movement? This is the question we will address in the following chapter.

Eleven

The Message of Holistic Health

Pir Vilayat Khan, spiritual leader of the Sufi Order in the West, was standing in the bright limelight of the stage and opened the congress with the official invocation:

> Toward the One, the perfection of Love, Joy, Harmony, and Beauty, in communion with all the illuminated souls, the hierarchy of the spiritual government of the world - Rama, Krishna, Shiva, the great Rishis and authors of the Vedas, Buddha, Hermes, Plato, Socrates, Plotinus, Pythagoras, Zoroaster, Noah, Enoch, Abraham, Moses, Melchizedek, Elijah, Ezechiel, Isaiah, Jesus Christ and the other Christian saints and martyrs... Mohammed, Ali, and the Sufis...[1]

You might want to know what kind of a congress was opened with such an incredible spiritual and theological amalgamation. In the hall were no ecstatic hippies worshipping a new Guru, but 3000 listeners of all ages and social backgrounds, 60 percent of them doctors and nurses. They had met, in September 1977, for a conference sponsored by the Association for Holistic Health (AHH) in San Diego. The theme of the congress: *Experiencing the Medical Model of the Future - An In-Depth Survey of Holistic Health.*

Lectures on the philosophical and scientific foundations of Holistic Health were complemented by seminars and practical exercises in acupuncture, reflexology, herbal medicine, bio-feedback, Transcendental Meditation, Yoga, psychic healing, hypnosis and more.

The yearning for a New Medicine

The programme offered by this "Association for Holistic Health" attempted to meet the needs of many people in the Western world. Never before has humanity been so open for a new medicine, a new message of hope and salvation, as in our days. For too long, body and spirit have been torn apart. Hospital medicine has restored man's physical health but failed to minister to his spiritual needs. The yearning for a wholesome philosophy of life, a wholesome treatment of man, is growing more and more.

The restoration of perfect health has attained a pivotal significance. He who promises to heal man's manifold ailments and give him hope for "perfect health" (Transcendental Meditation), will attract the crowds. Never before have people flocked to the healers as in our days.

But what is the philosophy behind the boom of the New Medicine? Why are there such overt religious overtones?

The coming world-religion

The Bible predicts that there will be a new world religion developing in the last days. In the book of Revelation, the Apostle John describes the "Mystery Babylon", characterised by ultimate totalitarianism, in which political power, economic control, religious worship, occult enlightenment, psychic powers and a world leader with an almost irresistible charisma will be combined. Brooks Alexander, director of the California-based Spiritual Counterfeits Project, writes: "This coming great World-Religion will offer itself to us as the 'Ancient Wisdom,' the 'Hidden Truth' underlying all the religious forms of history. In actual fact, however, it is not truth in any sense of the word, but a lie."[2]

Increasingly, observers of our society are under the impression that the prophecies of revelation will soon come true. Thus, influential Swiss mystic and professor of psychosomatic medicine, Dr. Balthasar Staehelin, writes:

"We are inevitably approaching *an all-encompassing world religion*, following the ever-same inward urge of humanity, and accordingly *one single political country which is the world...*"[3]

There are powerful New Age forces who are now uniting to launch the "Planetary Initiative for the World We Choose"[4] with the decided goal "to enlist people of many persuasions to join in support of a vision of humanity united to share a livable future on this planet." A quick glance over the list of supporting groups shows the strong religious emphasis of this effort. Among them are all major Holistic Health movements of the U.S. and Britain.

Brooks Alexander is convinced that the principles which were used by the serpent in the temptation of Adam and Eve in the garden of Eden, will reappear in the world-religion of the future:

> The deception is single in its nature, but it has six salient features (three of negation and three of affirmation). These may by analysed as follows:
> 1. The denial of the reality of the curse of death;
> 2. The denial of the truthfulness of God;
> 3. The denial of the loving kindness of God;
> 4. The promise of wisdom;
> 5. The promise of divinity; and
> 6. The promise of power - in that order.[5]

The future world religion will be governed by the principle of *monism**. In the assumption that "all is one", Satan and hell have no more room. Good and evil are both coming from the same divine source. God is not the personal Creator as He revealed in the Bible, but an impersonal power which permeates the whole universe and everything that lives in it.

---

* Monism (from *mono* = one), in a spiritual framework always refers to the fundamental tenet of classical occult philosophy that "All is One", and more significantly, the idea that God is not separate from his creation.

Death is denied and man is comforted with the idea of *reincarnation*, giving him a chance to improve in the next life. Meditation will unite all people and lead them to "enlightenment", giving them psychic powers and finally the illusion that *they themselves are divine*.

In the wake of this new world-religion "there will appear false Christs and false prophets, and perform great signs and miracles to deceive even the elect - if that were possible," says Jesus Christ in His famous discourse on the last times.[6]

Miraculous healings will prepare the way for this world system. If somebody is able to heal a person, the patient will, consciously or not, take his philosophical-religious beliefs into his own world-view. And the healers are constantly reminding their patients in books and magazines, in radio and TV as well as in personal conversations: "If it works, it's right!"

Forerunners of a coming world religion?

Are the healers really right? Or is the "Medicine of the Future" as it is called by the Holistic Health movement, only a forerunner for a coming "planetary" religion? Are the miracles they are purportedly performing really a message from God? Or are they preparing the way for other forces to take over?

Why is it so important to be "unprejudiced," "open," "spiritually passive," and "believing?" Why is faith playing such an important role in healing?

In order to give an answer to these questions we have to examine the philosophical underpinnings of Holistic Health and find out what the message is that the healers are bringing to their patients and the world.

Nobody can deny that the "New Medicine" is much more than a mere system of unorthodox healing methods. The spiritual aspects of the movement are too obvious. Dr. Mark Duke writes about acupuncture:

> The acupuncturist... brings his patients
> back to health not only for their own sake

and happiness, but so that the whole world may function properly. Every needle the acupuncturist twirls between his fingers bears the heavy weight of universal harmony in its slim, pointed end.[7]

Even when some methods seem so very "scientific and neutral", "it is our conviction," the researchers of SCP are writing, "that nothing in the universe stands apart from spiritual reality or is without spiritual implications. All things, whether material or nonmaterial, ultimately have their meaning defined by their relation to God and his purpose."[8]

For a better understanding of the Holistic message we have to answer the following questions:

1. What is their source of truth?
2. What are they teaching about God and the universe?
3. What are they saying about man?
4. How do they regard the problem of sin?
5. What is the way to salvation?

When I am using the term Holistic Health in a rather generalising way, I am fully aware that there will always be some individuals in this colourful and multi-faceted movement who will not express the thoughts I am going to delineate in exactly the same words I am using. Nevertheless, in my reading of hundreds of books and articles, I was struck by the fact that the teachings generally resemble one another to a high degree. They are woven into the whole fabric of Holistic Health like a golden thread.

Is the source of truth in the East?

Dr. Oyle spent twenty years as a family physician in New York. He felt increasingly the gnawing uncertainty as to whether the medical system he had been taught at the university was really providing an answer for his patients' problems. Today, Dr. Oyle is convinced that the Western approach to healing has reached a dead-end, and we need a whole new medical approach if any further progress is to ensue. He is now director of the Headlands Healing Service in California where he is investigating the application of high frequency waves in acupuncture.[9]

His new approach to medical progress has led him into the *East*. This is where ancient wisdom had been hidden for thousands of years, wisdom that could help man to renewed health. His new gospel is Eastern philosophy.

Dr. Voegeli, a prominent Swiss homoeopath, once ran a busy private X-ray clinic in Zurich. Today he is disillusioned with Western medicine. It is his conviction that there is more to disease and healing than physically and chemically measurable values. But:

> the scientists don't like to talk about these issues. Everyone has his personal ideas but officially they are ignored... Much more comprehensive and satisfying concepts have been developed in the East, especially in India. The Sankhya philosophy has extensively dealt with these problems...[10]

Dr. Voegeli and Dr. Oyle are two examples standing for thousands of naturopaths, "Holistic" practitioners or "psychic healers" who are walking the same way. Take any practitioner of alternative medicine, scratch the medical veneer, and you will find New Age philosophy beneath the surface. Disappointed in Western materialism, and unsatisfied by a church that is choked by tradition and liberal theology, the healers are turning to other sources. They are quite happy to embrace, instead, Eastern religions.

Their boldness to proclaim this message is growing: not to some idealistic followers of a Guru but to millions of people like you and me who are as disillusioned with Western thinking as they are.

Controlled?

With an uncanny unity, the New Age healers have turned to the Eastern model. They don't even know one another but they express the same ideas. They try to confine themselves to new medical techniques but their philosophical underpinnings are constantly coming to the surface. The source of truth, for the New Age practitioners, is in the East, whether they are prepared to admit it or not.

Together with occult physicists, liberal theologians, parapsychologists, UFO-believers and gurus they have become "voices in the technological wilderness" who shout, "Prepare ye the way of the philosophy of the New Age!" Despite all the external differences, they speak in such unison that one cannot escape the question as to whether there is more to it than mere personal conviction. Various authors[11,12] express it openly: are they controlled by a supernatural, transcendental power? Is their message so united because they have opened up to the same ungodly spirit?

Even those practitioners and physicians who do not really want to have any part with this philosophical system unconsciously provide, with their genuine and imagined success, the proof that New Age philosophy is the new way to health. One could almost coin the slogan, "If you care about your health, go East!"

This is no exaggeration. There is hardly any book on the therapies which are described here, that does not contain overt or covert references to Yoga, Eastern meditation and obviously occult practices. More and more people convey the opinion that truth is not to be regarded as absolute. Many disagree that the Bible is God's only answer to man's problems. A poll conducted among university students revealed that more than 50 percent were unconsciously holding an Eastern world view:[13] everything is relative, there are no absolutes. Why shouldn't truth be found in other philosophies? Why shouldn't Buddhism and Hinduism have valid answers to our problems?

These questions are intriguing - "Why actually not?" Even professing Christians who venture into biological healing get sucked into the attraction of those teachings. "I am a Catholic," says one producer of biological juice, "but I have studied all religions. I have gradually realised: Truth is much too wide to be pressed into one source. Let's search for the pearls and use them in our daily life."[14]

The Bible offers a clear answer in the quest for truth. Jesus says: "I am the way and the truth and the life. No one comes to the Father except through me."[15] And later, the Apostles confirm this proclamation with the following words: "Salvation is found in no one else, for there is no other name under heaven given to men by which we must be saved."[16]

But the Scriptures also describe, from Genesis to Revelation, how man yielded to the question of the serpent: "Did God really say...?" The prophet Jeremiah gives us God's comment: "My people have committed two sins: they have forsaken me, the spring of living water, and have dug their own cisterns, broken cisterns that cannot hold water."[17]

Is God only a cosmic energy field?

With Eastern philosophy, many practitioners have also adopted the Eastern concept of God. He is not a personal loving God who is concerned about man, but an impersonal "vital force", or a "cosmic energy."

John Keel, a respected parapsychological researcher and author, summarises what many are thinking:

> The standard definition of God, 'God is light,' is just a simple way of saying that God is energy. Electromagnetic energy. He is not a He but an It; a field of energy that permeates the entire universe and, perhaps, feeds off the energy generated by its component parts.[18]

For Holistic Health, God, energy, universe and nature are terms that can be used interchangeably. "Bioplasm", "Aura" or "Orgone" sound scientific but basically express the same notion. When acupuncturists talk about "cosmic energy" and psychic healers use "prana" they are using words that carry the notion of their concept of God. In her *Foot-Book*, Devaki Berkson says: "We all possess healing powers of the universe within us, and we all have the right and ability to call upon the healing power of God, nature, or whatever we feel comfortable calling it."[19]

The New Age concept of God is in no way different from the Hindu's idea of "Brahman" and Lao-Tse's teaching of the universal cosmic soul "Tao." And like Hinduism, Holistic Medicine is based on the concept that "All is one." There is no difference between creator and creation. Every being is permeated by divine energy. Somehow we are all a part of God. According to the Holistic mind sciences man's highest goal is the realisation that he himself is God. The serpent's whispered words of old are hissed in a new form into humanity's itching ears: "You will be like God..."[20]

There is no way to integrate the Christian faith with the monistic concept of God that is held by the New Age healers. The Bible does not reveal God as an unpersonal energy, in which both good and evil have their source. Rather, we are confronted with a mighty Creator who is holy and pure. "God is light; in him is no darkness at all," writes the Apostle John.[21] Man is not a part of God but His creation. Jesus Christ is not a prophet among many other deities and saints; He is the Son of God, who alone shows us the way back to God: "For God so loved the world that he gave his one and only Son, that whoever believes in him shall not perish but have eternal life."[22]

Man - spark of the universal spirit?

"Our spirit is a spark of the universal spirit, the individual soul a spark of the soul of God," says psychic healer Ursula Kress.[23] "Consciousness/matter/God is diffused throughout the universe and tends towards increasing complexity, and by a quantum jump (birth) makes itself a body, man." This is how acupuncturist Dr. Oyle sees man.[24]

The New Age practitioners express themselves

differently, some scientifically, some mystically, but basically they are conveying the same: man is only a part of God, like a drop taken from an ocean. Man is diffused by the all-permeating divine energy, a tiny wheel in the grand cosmic machine. The logical consequence is the assumption that man is like a football kicked around by cosmic forces. The stars in the infinite universe determine the fate of man whose body is a small world in itself.

The same concept is applied to man and his organs. Thus iridologist Dr. Beer writes:

> In the same way as man has to be regarded as a small world (a microcosm) in relation to the universe, we have to perceive the eye as a microcosm related to individual man, reflecting the condition of his soul and body. As the whole is influencing the part, the part has its repercussions on the whole...[25]

With this view of man the natural healers have raised the ancient cornerstones of astrology, magic and divination to new honours. The old mysteries of Babylon's astrologers are in full bloom again in the 20th century.

Re-interpretation of life

Disease, healing and death have taken on a new meaning, the "holistic" world-view. French physician and Christian author Dr. Christian Klopfenstein writes:

> When one believes that the human microcosm is reflecting macrocosm, this conception which reduces all organisms to automatisms, one is led back into heathenism, seeing the whole world as governed by the stars and the planets; back into regulated automatism and absolute fatalism.
>
> It is a world without spirit, without

> conscience, without goal or meaning, a world of robots, a world of idol-worshippers, of the 'slaves of fate and the stars', of antique heathenism and the adherents of the mechanistic philosophy of modern neo-heathenism.[26]

Within the framework of Eastern philosophy, *disease* has no finite meaning, rather it is the inevitable "karma". With this term the Hindus are describing fate. Every deed, every word and every thought has its consequences: what man sows, he reaps. His mistakes cause the balance of divine energy to tilt, and he becomes sick. We have encountered this thought over and over again in the previous chapters.

Healing attains a new significance: it is more than the mere restoration of man, it is actually *an act of salvation*: the harmony with the divine universe is restored, the divine can now flow unobstructedly again. Needles and massage, homoeopathic potencies and radionic boxes, they all are to help man attain a new unity with the cosmos, with God.

Often, however, this unity cannot be accomplished in one life alone. It is not surprising therefore, that many healers have adopted the idea of *reincarnation*, of a rebirth after death. Man then has a new chance to make up for the faults of his previous life and thus to move the wheel of fate to the next notch.

In summary, the "holistic" view of man does not square with the teachings of Scripture. The Bible states very clearly that man is not a part of God, he is his creation. He is not a ball tossed around by cosmic forces, but has a free will enabling him to decide between good and evil, between God and his opponent Satan. Man's disease is not without meaning (see chapter 12), and healing is not automatically indicating harmony with God's will.

The message of reincarnation is equally deceptive, giving man the delusive hope that there will be a chance in his next life to get straight with God. But the Bible says, "Man is destined to die once, and after that to face judgement."[27] We have only this life. Our decision here on earth determines our future in eternity.

The problem of sin

Eastern philosophy doesn't know the concept of sin in the Biblical sense. This is impressively demonstrated in a lecture of Hindu-philosopher Vivekenanda which he gave at the world congress of religions in Chicago 1893:

> Listen, children of eternal bliss!... Allow me, brothers, to address you with this sweet name... The Hindu refuses to call you sinners; you are children of God, partakers of immortal bliss, holy and perfect beings. You are deities on earth - Sinners? It is a sin to call a man by this name; it is a permanent desecration of human nature...[28]

Guru Maharishi Mahesh Yogi, the founder of Transcendental Meditation, whose teachings have many followers among "holistic" practitioners, sees the causes of poverty, disease, hatred, exploitation and war not in the basic sinful nature of man. To him these permanent problems of humanity have their roots in a psychological defect.

But Holistic Health does not simply view man as perfect. Man is seen as an imperfect being, constantly making mistakes. While blocking the free flow of divine energy, his failures do not separate him from God. Living unhealthily is considered as sinning against one's body. Psychologist Konrad Lorenz talks of the eight cardinal sins of man.[29] Environmentalists denounce pollution as man's collective guilt (which is true!) Nutritionists fight dietary sins, the wrong composition of our food, artificial flavours and preservatives. "Through the reading of such books," writes Dr. Paul Tournier, "patients can become thoroughly obsessed. A new world of enemies has arisen: a grain of refined sugar, a tomato, a medical injection, a surgical operation, a pneumothorax,, are feared as if they were serious crimes."[30] But they evade the fact that our sin is eternally separating us from God.

Salvation - not necessary!

Consequently it is obvious that man's future is assessed differently by New Age practitioners than by the teachings of Jesus Christ. Where there is no Satan, there is no eternal condemnation; where there is no personal God, there is no judgement. Where there is no final death, there is no need for a decision in this life, for there will be many chances later. When there is no sin, there is no separation from God. And finally, if we are all permeated by divine energy, we do not need a way to reconciliation with God as we are already part of God.

It is the one and only goal of Holistic Medicine to show man the way to help him*self*. The basic message is, "You can help and save yourself!" The power of self-healing is slumbering in every person, like the serpent of Kundalini in Hinduism. The various healing methods only serve to discover and develop these latent psychic powers.

Yoga and Meditation are supposed to help the seeking patient to find himself and to overcome his psychological defects as well as his physical ailments. Through "holistic" treatment he is to return to a state of energetic balance, to harmony with the universe and supposed oneness with God.

These teachings are as addictive as sweet wine, and millions have readily embraced them. They are a message that people like to hear, for which their ears are "itching", as the Bible puts it. And the cures of psychic healers and Holistic practitioners are the signs and miracles which confirm these teachings.

Marriage of science and religion

The intoxicating drink of Eastern philosophy was pressed in the occult teachings of the astrologists of Babylon; it was served again and again in the mystical cults and religions throughout the centuries. It inspired the alchemists and influenced many a great poet and philosopher, such as Goethe and Kant.[31] Today the old wine is filling new scientific wine-skins.

It is the goal of Holistic Health, says the president of the Association of Holistic Health, David Harris, to arrange a *marriage of science with religion*.[32] And former astronaut Edgar Mitchell who is now doing research on the occult, comments: "Now is the time to develop our non-rational abilities into a 'subjective technology,' which will begin the *wedding of science and religion*, reason and intuition, the physical and the spiritual."[33]

Similar statements were made at the second world congress of natural healing 1976, in Switzerland. "The *integration of the esoteric and of science is possible*," stated French homoeopath Michaud, "and homoeopathy has to play an important role as the link between the two ways of thinking."[34]

This goal is not only pursued by back-alley healers and occult orientated scientists. Even physicists in renowned institutes of East and West are devoting themselves to the investigation of the occult with the help of modern nuclear physics. Einstein has become the new Stone of Wisdom. His theory of relativity is being bent to serve as scientific justification of the old monistic formula, "All is One."

Take any publication on the interrelations of science, medicine and occultism: there are plenty of doctors and professors quoted. It does not seem to disturb the New Age to take random quotations out of their context and use them in support of their teachings. Not infrequently, in their search for knowledge and enlightenment, the truth is run over.

Whether they are engaged in Transcendental Meditation or do research on acupuncture, the New Age physicists are pursuing *one* goal which was once defined by American physicist Dr. Jack Sarfatti, who said, "We want to infect society with a different view of reality. Physicists are the high-priests of society."[35]

But Sarfatti's new view of reality is in fact old mystical wisdom: Buddha's enlightenment, the God-consciousness of the Hindus, the light of Zen-meditation. The fading idol of Western civilisation, science, is helping the new god of Eastern philosophy to climb the stirrups of the horse of power.

Preparation for the anti-christ?

The description of the basic beliefs in the Holistic health movement is not dry and unnecessary theory. Rather, it is extremely important to understand the background of the current vogue of signs and miracles in our world.

Whereas the health practitioners in past decades were rather regarded as "quacks" now almost no day goes by without a report on their "miracles." And people today are open to miracles again. The more they are disappointed with the unfulfilled promises of science, the more open they are to the transcendental world. There is no other way to explain the success of Uri Geller or Erich von Daeniken. Infinitely amplified by the mass-media, they are opening for the spiritually hungry individual a window to the world beyond.

The faith in miracles is one of the seven pillars of occult philosophy, writes occultist Marc Edmund Jones.

> *Healing* in consequence has been the cornerstone of the esoteric tradition throughout the ages. The seeker is expected to see beyond all the normal boundaries of self, visualising a reality, and a truth, which may continually reveal themselves to him through the miracles of his private accomplishment. As a first step towards the greater mysteries he claims and demonstrates a simple *Health, Prosperity* and *Happiness*, and enters upon the way of understanding.[36]

Even many Christians succumb to religiously camouflaged deceivers, when they make miraculous healings the centre of their faith, and fall prey to their desire for healing at any price. All too often, in their intoxicated enthusiasm over miraculous healings, they depart from the Biblical way of wholesome healing (see chapter 12).

Even scholars who are not professing Christians are recognising the dangers of an exploitation of this blind readiness to believe in miracles. Thus, German professor of psychosomatic medicine and author of several best-sellers, Dr. Horst-Eberhard Richter, writes:

> There are indications that the uncritical exploitation of the attractivity of sensational phenomena are causing infinitely more harm than many horror thrillers or pornographic movies. The epidemiological readiness to uncritical submission and the faith in miracles are the ideal culture medium, not only for clairvoyants, psychokinetics or miraculous healers, but no less for *demagogues of an incomparably more dangerous format*. Remember: In the beginning came Hanussen...[37]

What did Professor Richter mean with these words? To understand them we have to go back into the history of the Third Reich. Jan Erik Hanussen was a spiritistic medium who had a far-reaching influence on the decisions of the "Fuehrer". Known as the "prophet of the Third Reich" he gave public performances in the Berlin Scala where he convinced thousands of his abilities as a clairvoyant and thought reader. He was said to be the man who largely contributed to Hitler's seizing power by revealing to him the thoughts and intentions of his opponents. In the beginning came Hanussen; then the Fuehrer appeared.

> They do not know it yet - the acupuncturists, what principles they are working with,... the iridologists, who are examining visible radiations; the dowsers who sense hidden vibrations - but they are all *forerunners of a revelation in the medical world-view*.[38]

This is how a New Age healer perceives Holistic Health. While scholars are still arguing over the genuineness of the placebo effect in the healers' miracles; while Christians are still discussing the pros and cons of occult bondage through acupuncture or homoeopathy - there is a subtle *turning of the masses towards a new world view* which is proclaimed by the New Age movement and supported by its healers' miracles.

Hardly anybody can escape its wake. Submitting to treatment on an Eastern basis or practising Eastern forms of meditation will probably not directly bring a person into direct contact with occult powers or even lead to possession. But there are other spiritual consequences which are at least as dangerous: the patient is spiritually turned around, opening himself consciously or unconsciously to the "wine of prostitution" served by the "whore of Babylon", as the Bible expresses itself drastically,[39] to all people in the wake of the antichrist.

Therefore, it is high time that Christians discern the poisonous drink of "monism" and return to the Word of God. The Bible calls on us to put on the whole armour of God to resist the cunning attacks of Satan. The message of the Bible is clearly opposed to the philosophy of New Age healing.

Jesus Christ is the only way to God. He has proclaimed God's love and His plan for us. He came into this world to save us through His death on the cross. The path to God is not leading over an elusive harmony with the universe through homoeopathy, massage or acupuncture, through yoga or meditation. In our own strength, we will never get right with God. The Bible says, "There is one God and one mediator between God and men, the man Christ Jesus who gave himself as a ransom for all men."[40]

Freedom from stress and disease is not salvation. Holistic Medicine is "hollow-istic" treatment unless it deals with the root-cause of man's separation from God and offers the true solution for his problems. Only when a person confesses his sin, entrusts his life to Christ and finds the fulfillment of his needs in Him, will he truly live in harmony with God.

Twelve

Healing at any Price?

Carpenter Arnold Brown is an example[1] of man's desperate search for healing. He is 29 years old, pale and lank. He complains of a constant stomach ache, which he describes as a feeling of distention, and at times a dull, throbbing pain. During the night the pain often develops into excruciating colic. He is not able to get much sleep and his efficiency at work has dropped off. Sometimes he succeeds in suppressing the pain by drinking beer. He dares not eat any more and has consequently lost a lot of weight over the years. So far Mr. Brown has consulted about twenty doctors. He has seen several health practitioners and has gone through five hospitalisations and several courses of treatment at health spas - all to no avail.

The diagnoses varied from "gastritis", "nervous stomach-complaints", "subacidity", "suspected ulcer", to "disease of the pancreas", "liver and gall-bladder ailment", "suspected porphyria" and "vegetative dystonia". Everyone said something different, and each one suggested a new therapy. Usually there was some improvement at the beginning, but in the long run they all failed to help. Following the advice of a professor, he abandoned his own business and went back to a less demanding position. But this move did not result in improvement either.

Mr. Brown is desperate, lost, and he tells doctor No. 21 he will continue his search for the proper medicine and help even if he has to go outside the medical profession.

Why is there disease?

Mr. Brown's medical history has a background we will deal with a little later. But let us first turn to the question that disturbs and puzzles so many people:

Why is there disease and suffering at all? Why are Christians not exempted from sickness? Why does God, seem to be a cosmic sadist who watches with crossed arms as the human worm writhes in pain? Why is life so unjust, afflicting one and sparing another?

Streams of ink have flown in an attempt to answer these questions. I am not a theologian, so do not expect a learned discourse with scores of unintelligible words and extensive bibliographic references. I am a young physician who has read quite a few books on the subject and has discussed the problem with experienced physicians and counsellors. I have sat at the bedside of many a patient, and I remain deeply convinced that the Bible is God's message to man. And still there are times when I stand numbed by inconceivable suffering, unable to help, awkwardly trying to understand and to comfort, yet painfully aware that I don't have the ultimate answer. Often I can only identify with the great apostle and theologian, St. Paul: "Now we see but a poor reflection; then we shall see face to face. Now I know in part; then I shall know fully, even as I am fully known."[2]

Thorns and thistles - and bacteria

Nevertheless, it is possible to sketch a few rough lines on the question of 'why there is suffering'. Whether we like it or not, we are affected by the Fall. We are still bearing the consequences of Adam and Eve's disobedience.

The world in which we live is under the curse of God. The ground not only produces thorns and thistles, but has become the abode of all sorts of germs. The once perfect body of man has become brittle and susceptible to disease. Death has entered the world, accompanied by its heralds of sickness and old age.

Christians live in this world, even if they are not of the world any more. When a person is converted he is not miraculously freed from the power of gravity. In the same way, a Christian is not exempt from physical affliction. Paul writes: "We know that the whole creation has been groaning as in the pains of childbirth right up to the present time. Not only so, but we ourselves, who have the first fruits of the Spirit, groan inwardly as we wait eagerly for our adoption as sons, the redemption of our bodies."[3]

Preventable diseases

Many diseases strike people at random, believers and nonbelievers alike. They can vary in severity from the common cold to the tragedy of multiple sclerosis.

Other afflictions, however, are clearly *caused by sin*. How many people invite disease as a result of their sinful way of life, only to complain that God was watching their sufferings without compassion. An excellent book on this topic has been written by American physician Dr. S. J. McMillen. The title is *None of these diseases*.[4]

It is appalling to realise how many diseases could be prevented by a different lifestyle. Cancer of the lung would practically disappear if *cigarette smoking* were abandoned. Today's world-wide consumption totals 4000 billion cigarettes per year. About 100 billion dollars are actually puffed into the air as smoke.

Let's take another vice, alcohol. Approximately 8-10 percent of the men in Western countries have to be regarded as alcoholics. Untold suffering is caused by this "comforter" in families and personal lives! Psychiatric clinics are full of alcoholic ruins. A large percentage of accidents are caused by drunk driving. And if you ever happen to see a drunkard end his wretched life in a hepatic coma, you will not easily forget its terrible impression.

Rising living standards lead more and more people into *excessive eating*, resulting in a veritable string of diseases: high blood pressure, arteriosclerosis, heart attacks, diabetes, hyperuricemia (gout) and dental caries to mention only a few. Since the turn of our century the percentage of diabetics has risen fifteen times!

The increase of *venereal disease* is another area of concern. Just a few years ago doctors, with the help of modern antibiotics, were confidently controlling those who were affected. But now this disease seems to be spreading more than ever, due to the current sexual "freedom". Even more serious is the fact that now there are organisms which have proved to be resistant to all known remedies.

Guilt as a cause of illness

Most of the diseases which family physicians see in their private practices have to do with the changed lifestyle of our time. More than fifty percent of all patients suffer from *psychosomatic diseases*. The triggers may vary, but they often have their origins in the loss of meaningful relationships, and people's turning their back on God.

"God has a purpose for our life, as he has for the world," writes Swiss physician and counsellor Paul Tournier.[5] "And if the world is sick today because it is disobeying God's laws, men too are sick, because they do not live in accordance with God's purpose."

Tournier illustrates this with many anecdotes from his patients' lives. These are included in his easy to read, yet profound book, *The Healing of Persons*. I am convinced that this book is probably of greater value to many patients than a large bottle of tranquillizers.

It is the unrest of our time, the loneliness, stress, worries, anxieties, and the lack of deep relationships which constitute some of the major causes of psychosomatic illnesses. And in addition, there is often an undealt-with past, and *unforgiven guilt*.

Let's go back to Mr. Brown: a closer look at his life history uncovers the root of his tenacious stomach problem. The patient had a very strained relationship with his father all through his life. After an argument over a minor issue, Mr. Brown avoided his parents for two long years.

When he was 20, he had his first sexual relationship with a widowed lady, and felt very guilty as a result of it. Subsequently he obtained a job with a carpenter, who took him into his family and treated him like a son. During this time Mr. Brown's father died of stomach cancer. Soon he became involved in a passionate love-affair with his boss's neglected wife and when they had their first sexual encounter, he not only reacted with severe feelings of guilt, but also with ferocious stomach pain, which was to remain with him.[6]

The meaning of illness

It would be wrong to view illness as God's crackdown on infidel sinners only. As Christians, our first question should not aim at the *why* of suffering but at the *purpose*.

I am convinced that God allows some illnesses to bring people to a place where they can listen in their heart to what He has to tell them. In this way suffering can lead to a strengthening of faith.

Have you ever asked God to show you what He wants to tell you through your suffering? Is your lifestyle too fast and hurried, without time for God? Is it guilt that prevents you from sleeping? Are there problems you have not given over to the Lord?

Another reason why God may allow suffering is illustrated in the life of Job. Hospital-counsellor Dr. Laubach says that *trials of endurance:*

> are to help a person thrust himself completely into the powerful hand of God... As we know, the spiritual darkness during Job's journey of suffering became so overwhelming at times that he began accusing God. But the Lord, in His wonderful mercy, did not abandon him. The Bible makes it clear that God may permit illnesses in the lives of His children, thus leading the believer into a kind of 'stress-testing' to the brink of man's ability to cope. Job's trial illustrates the words of Jesus where He said, 'You do not realise now what I am doing, but later you will understand'.[7]

Another aspect of suffering is that God uses it to *teach us lessons* we could not learn otherwise. People who are quick to judge others often learn compassion only after they have gone through a trying affliction themselves. Our infirmities teach us how transient this world is, and that there are riches far beyond material gain and physical health. Here is another quote from Dr. Laubach: "Illness in the life of the believer helps him to focus his eyes on the coming glory of God and to help him steadfastly claim the promises of the prophetic word."[8]

Healing for body and soul

Although disease can be seen as a blessing in some cases, we should not surrender to our fate by savouring, in self-destructive asceticism, every drop of the bitter cup. Healing is an important part of the Christian message. Wherever Jesus went, He healed the sick. To his disciples He gave the commission, not only to proclaim the message of the coming kingdom of heaven, but to heal the afflicted as well. The apostles carried on this tradition, and miraculous healings accompanied their message.

One characteristic stands out in the Biblical account of the miracles: healing was always related to the message of salvation. When Jesus healed the paralytic who had been brought by his four friends, He first assured him of the forgiveness of his sins. The healing of the soul had first priority in Christ's ministry. But to demonstrate to the watching crowd that He was indeed the Messiah and had the right to forgive sin, He restored the lame man's health.

How many patients, among them many Christians, are searching for healing at any price in our days! Their concern for physical health is barely covered by the loincloth of Christian rites and words. R.A. Torrey, former superintendent of the Moody Bible Institute, sadly states in his booklet *Divine Healing*: "Human nature is just the same today as when our Lord was on the earth. Multitudes, unnumbered multitudes, crowded about Him, journeying many miles to see Him in the hope of getting healing for their bodies, but very, very few were eager for the salvation of their soul."[9] In one incident Jesus gave a dramatic illustration of His priorities: "It is better for you to enter life maimed or crippled than to have two hands or two feet and be thrown into eternal fire."[10]

Miraculous healing

Now then, have all miraculous healings through the power of God ceased? Are modern-day healings merely psychosomatic phenomena or demonic counterfeits?

Some Christians maintain that Jesus not only bore our sins on the cross but our diseases as well. A real Christian therefore need never be sick. They believe that illness today is a sign of lack of faith.

Rational theologians and many physicians, on the other hand, believe that the miracles of Jesus can be explained naturally and that the diseases He healed were either of a psychosomatic nature, or that the accounts were simply fabricated. According to them, these miracles didn't happen then and miracles don't happen today.

It is always dangerous to go to an extreme. To claim that every Christian has to be completely healthy, is to stick one's head in the sand and ignore the facts. How many tears have been caused by the messages of healing-fanatics! How often do those messages drive patients even further away from God into the darkness of doubt, confusion and fear or into a frantic search for healing at any price!

Completely denying miracles is even more unrealistic. Consider the logic of Juri Gagarin, the first Soviet cosmonaut, who proclaimed after his return from space: "There is no God. I have not seen him!" I have personally read and heard several accounts by reliable people who have witnessed miraculous healings. It is impossible to simply discard them.

Miracles are not and never have been the rule. They seem to occur more frequently, however, in areas where the gospel is being presented for the first time, as in crusade evangelism. In such a case, as in the days of the early church, they serve the purpose of planting and supporting the Christian message. Genuine miracles have nothing in common with the healing frenzy that is taking place in the religiously over-stimulated West today.

The New Testament records that as the gospel spread,

and was made increasingly available in written form, fewer supernatural occurences took place. Despite his spiritual power, Paul had his "beloved physician" Luke with him. He obviously suffered from some form of disease and, despite repeated prayers, God did not give him perfect health. He did, however, say, "My grace is sufficient for you, for my power is made perfect in weakness."[11] Nor were his co-workers spared from serious illnesses: Paul had to leave his associate Trophimus in Miletus because he was too sick to travel,[12] and young church-leader Timothy often suffered from a stomach ailment and "frequent illnesses."[13]

The Bible does not oppose medicine

John Stott, the respected British theologian, once stated: "All healing is divine healing, whether without the use of, or through the use of, physical, psychological or surgical means."[14]

Christian surgeon Gordon Scorer[15] differentiates between "natural healing" and "miraculous healing" but believes both are caused by God. Through His Son Jesus Christ God has worked genuine miracles, and it is presumptuous to classify every healing that does not have an overt connection with Christian faith, as not worked by God.

Is it not the Creator who has equipped our bodies with so many wonderful immune mechanisms? Paracelsus once wrote:

> God should actually be the highest and most important physician to you Christians; the most powerful and not the least; nothing happens without Him. The heathens and the ungodly can call humans to their rescue - you, however, should cry to God, and He will send you the one who will heal you, be it a saint, physician or Himself.[16]

The Arabic language has a beautiful expression for the

physician, "wasta", describing him as "mediator" between God's healing power and the patient. Whoever or whatever is the means for healing, the glory belongs to the Creator of our bodies. Without these wonderful inbuilt cell-mechanisms all medical efforts would be in vain.

It is not a sign of unbelief to consult a doctor in the event of illness. Dr. Paul Tournier does not see an unsurmountable abyss between science and faith: To him:

> science, in the Biblical view, is a precious gift from God, entrusted to us so that we may better care for our patients. But with it goes the risk of losing that humility without which there can be no true science and no true medicine. This humility can be recovered only through the reflection of our own conduct, the repentance spoken of throughout the Bible.[17]

The Bible is not opposed to remedies. When king Hezekiah was about to die, God sent him, upon his request, the prophet Isaiah. Hezekiah was not healed by a miracle in the strict sense of the word, but, as Isaiah said, "prepare a poultice of figs and apply it to the boil, and he will recover."[18]

The apostle Paul, inspired by the Holy Spirit, wrote to Timothy: "Stop drinking only water, and use a little wine because of your stomach and your frequent illnesses."[19] Today we know that grape juice and wine contain substances which are very effective against bacteria and viruses.

A proper balance is of primary importance. After his recovery, King Hezekiah did not lavishly praise the prophet Isaiah for the excellent job he had done, or the sensational natural remedy "poultice of figs". He rather gave thanks to God for his regained health: "Lord, by such things men live; and my spirit finds life in them too. You restored me to health and let me live. Surely it was for my benefit that I suffered such anguish. In your love you kept me from the pit of destruction; you have put all my sins behind your back."[19]

The value of physician and remedies in relation to God is beautifully described in the Apocrypha:

> Honour the doctor for his services, for the Lord created him. His skill comes from the Most High, and he is rewarded by kings... The Lord has created medicines from the earth, and a sensible man will not disparage them... The Lord has imparted knowledge to men that by their use of His marvels He may receive praise; by using them the doctor relieves pain and from them the pharmacist makes up his mixture. There is no end to the works of the Lord, who spreads health over the whole world.[20]

Isn't it strange? For many Christians it is natural to include a request for their daily bread when they say the Lord's prayer. They pray for it and thank God although they know that the flour is ground by the miller, and the dough is mixed, kneaded and baked by modern bakeries to be sold as bread in the grocery store. Why do we find it so difficult to ask God, with the same believing trust, to give wisdom to the physician so that he may prescribe the proper medication, and then fail to glorify Him when it helps?

Even more important than the restoration of our bodies is the healing of the soul. Paul Tournier says:

> Doubtless we may also see the merciful hand of God in the powerful drugs with which we may ease pain, arrest diarrhoea, stimulate a faltering heart, or produce a little sleep. But we must also be on our guard lest these aids drug the patient's conscience as well, blinding him to the need for reforming his way of life.[21]

But many patients simply are not willing to change their lives. They do not want to admit that their pain stems not so much from external causes, but rather from internal poisons such as worries, fears, guilt, bitterness and stress. They do want to be healthy, but they refuse to open up their lives to God and commit themselves to Him. They would rather try to pull themselves out of the mire by their own efforts.

It is these patients who often frequent the waiting-rooms of the naturopaths. And it is tragic when Christians, despite their knowledge of the origin of "Holistic" medicine, would rather seek help in Eastern methods than in talking their problems over with a counsellor.

Dangerous booby-traps

It is not uncommon that people who turn to psychic healers in their search for health experience a subtle shift in their priorities. Patients who are believers have to be particularly aware of this danger. Venturing into Holistic health is like entering a border-zone full of hidden booby traps that are apt to blow up without warning at any time.

The first trap is an *unhealthy bondage to people and remedies*. Many patients "swear by their homoeopath". Others are unwaveringly convinced they have found the "true healthy diet". And then it is so easy for healers and therapies to become substitute idols, as ways to live in harmony with the universe. "Cursed is the one," exclaims the prophet Jeremiah, "who trusts in man, who depends on flesh for his strength and whose heart turns away from the Lord!" And shortly after he prays: "Heal me, O Lord, and I will be healed; save me and I will be saved, for you are the one I praise!"[22]

The second trap is a consequence of the first one. It is alarming to see the *fanatic missionary zeal* displayed by patients who have gone to a psychic healer or who have had some good results with one of the latest fad-diets. When nature takes the place of God, natural medicine can really become "a religion, and an exceedingly fanatical one," to quote Paul Tournier.[23]

A practical example: after Mrs Patterson, an evangelical

Christian lady, had experienced an improvement of her headaches through reflexology, she purchased several books on the subject at 15 dollars each to send to her friends accompanied by an enthusiastic letter. It didn't seem to bother Mrs Patterson that the book also contained occult techniques along with the wonderful method that had brought her relief. I wondered if Mrs Patterson would have spent as much money to buy Christian books to send to her unsaved friends with the same enthusiasm?

Let's look at another example of a dear old Christian lady who for years had suffered from arthritic pain. We know today that worries, grief and bitterness, can greatly influence the intensity of arthritis. This woman experienced relief through acupuncture and felt revitalised. Today she takes children and grandchildren to her acupuncturist for every minor ailment. If only she would try to win them for Christ with the same fervour!

Another dangerous booby-trap is the *religious message of holistic health*. This has been extensively dealt with in chapter 11. Christians must be made aware that they will be treated for the most part with methods based on occult and Eastern philosophy when they consult a holistic healer. Thus they expose themselves to a possibly detrimental spiritual influence. Paul warned the Colossians: "See to it that no one takes you captive through hollow and deceptive philosophy, which depends on human tradition and the basic principles of this world rather than on Christ. For in Christ all the fullness of Deity lives in bodily form, and you have been given fullness in Christ."[24] We do well to heed this warning so appropriate to our subject.

Occult bondage

Certainly the most dangerous mine in the holistic field is the danger of *occult bondage*. So many people have paid the price of losing their inner peace in their search for healing. After patients have consulted a psychic, they often suffer from severe anxiety-attacks," a physician told me. "Then they come to me and want tranquillizers." They can develop an alarming dullness for spiritual things and display an increasing resistance to everything that has to do with Biblical truth. Especially patients who suffered from emotional weakness before they consulted an occult healer may experience a deterioration of their symptoms. Many times the relaxation they expected is only of short duration, soon giving way to increased inner tension.

Should you develop such symptoms after consulting a psychic healer, I would urge you to talk with an experienced pastoral counsellor. Consciously *renounce* every connection with occult powers and *re-dedicate* your life to Christ.

On the other hand, it is dangerous to blame all unexplained phenomena on demonic powers. We are critical of those psychiatrists who have abandoned the concept of sin and replaced it with the label of a psychological problem. A similar mistake is made by counsellors who all too frequently diagnose occult bondage in their clients, thus relieving them of all responsibility for their sinful behaviour.

Is there any way to *prevent occult bondage?* A former naturopath wrote to me: "Unfortunately many Christians are not able to discern if a healing method has been infiltrated by the enemy. They then fall prey to occult practitioners, especially when their first goal is health at any price instead of asking for God's will at any price."

Pastor Johann Christoph Blumhardt, who witnessed many wonderful healings, but also knew about the danger of demonic influence, writes:

> The power of demons is mighty only over the lustful and the curious; those who want to try and taste everything, not shying away from any snare, saying: 'Nothing can happen to me if I get involved in it!' Stay away from where you don't belong and where you sense something foreign. Why should you taste every new fad that comes along? Before you notice it, you will accept the one who brings the novelty as a saviour... If you

remain with your child-like faith in all
simplicity, as you have learned it from the
Scriptures of our fathers, no demon will
overpower you.[25]

What was Paul's opinion?

Some readers will probably tell me: "I have been under
treatment from a homoeopath for years, but my spiritual
life has not suffered. I know this man personally and am
convinced he does not employ occult practices. Should I
throw away all homoeopathic remedies?"

Others will write to me: "Somebody told me that a
certain company is producing their herbal teas with the
help of a radionic pendulum. Is that true? That herbal tea
has really helped me, and I have not noticed any negative
effect on my Christian life. Am I under occult bandage
because I have taken it?"

The first Christians in Corinth had similar, if not more
serious problems. They had to answer the question: Should
we eat the meat of animals that have been sacrificed in the
heathen temples? Were they risking occult bondage?

What was Paul's answer to them? Let's read what he
wrote in his first letter to the Corinthians:[26]

Therefore, my dear friends, flee from
idolatry. I speak to sensible people; judge
for yourselves what I say. Is not the cup of
thanksgiving for which we give thanks a
participation in the blood of Christ? And is
not the bread we break a participation in
the body of Christ? Because there is one
loaf, we, who are many, are one body, for
we all partake of the one loaf.

Consider the people of Israel: Do not
those who eat the sacrifices participate in
the altar? Do I mean then that a sacrifice
offered to an idol is anything, or that an
idol is anything? No but the sacrifices of
pagans are offered to demons, not to God,

and I do not want you to be participants with demons. You cannot drink the cup of the Lord and the cup of demons too; you cannot have a part in both the Lord's table and the table of demons. Are we trying to arouse the Lord's jealousy? Are we stronger than he?

'Everything is permissible' - but not everything is beneficial. 'Everything is permissible' - but not everything is constructive. Nobody should seek his own good but the good of others.

Eat anything sold in the meat market without raising questions of conscience, for, 'The earth is the Lord's, and everything in it.'

If some unbeliever invites you to a meal and you want to go, eat whatever is put before you without raising questions of conscience. But if anyone says to you, 'This has been offered in sacrifice,' then do not eat it, both for the sake of the man who told you and for conscience sake - the other man's conscience, I mean, not yours. For why should my freedom be judged by another's conscience? If I take part in the meal with thankfulness, why am I denounced because of something I thank God for?

So whether you eat or drink or whatever you do, do it all for the glory of God. Do not cause anyone to stumble, whether Jews, Greeks or the church of God - even as I try to please everybody in every way. For I am not seeking my own good but the good of many, so that they may be saved. Follow my example, as I follow the example of Christ.

Now replace the meat sacrificed to idols with

"homoeopathic remedies" or "herbal medicine" and re-read the text. You will have to decide for yourself if you want to continue to take these remedies after reading this book. No one else can make this decision for you.

More than remedies

As Christians, do we have an alternative? Do we have more to offer to sick and suffering people than medicines and deceitful reliance on new "miraculous cures"?

I think we do. The apostle James writes to the Christian churches:

> Is any of you sick? He should call the elders of the church to pray over him and anoint him with oil in the name of the Lord. And the prayer offered in faith will make the sick person well; the Lord will raise him up. If he has sinned, he will be forgiven. Therefore confess your sins to each other and pray for each other so that you may be healed. The prayer of a righteous man is powerful and effective.[27]

This paragraph describes four crucial aspects of healing from a Christian perspective. *First*, a rebuttal to the modern disease of isolation and loneliness. Christians need the fellowship of other believers. How many people try to solve their problems in their own little protective shell. They have no one to comfort or to encourage them, no one who would perhaps tell them: "What you are doing is not right."

These people tend to focus only on themselves and their problems, so it is not surprising at all when they suffer from all sorts of psychosomatic illnesses. To them I'd like to prescribe: "committed involvement in a living fellowship of Christians." They need to meet other people with their problems and to learn to understand them. They should join a Bible study group where they can explore and enjoy the promises of God! If they edge out of their protective shell and share their problems with others they will learn to turn away from themselves and experience God's presence in everyday life. And don't be surprised when suddenly the ailment they have suffered from for so many years loosens its grip, and their depression lifts.

A *second* step towards healing is *prayer*. What riches are there in talking with God! Sincere prayer does not bounce off the ceiling. God is there, and He hears everything you tell him.

Many people mull over their problems for years, repressing them until they develop into illness, for example duodenal ulcers. Christians, however, can bring their problems to God in prayer and unload their burden.

But prayer is more than a spiritual "hotline". It is here where we can express the things we are grateful for. Gratitude can turn around our whole basic attitude toward life. Paul wrote to the church in Ephesus that they should be "always giving thanks to God the Father, for everything, in the name of our Lord Jesus Christ."[28] Unloading our worries in prayer and expressing thanks to God for everything leads to a profound, unshakable peace in our hearts. These facts have been beautifully captured in Paul's words: "Do not be anxious about anything, but in everything, by prayer and petition, with thanksgiving, present your requests to God. And the peace of God, which transcends all understanding, will guard your hearts and your minds in Christ Jesus."[29] Prayer in this sense will do more for you than "positive thinking" and more than any in depth psycho-analysis!

Confession and forgiveness

Thirdly, the *confession of sin* and the *acceptance of forgiveness* plays a central role in James' description of God's therapeutic plan.

Many modern psychotherapists, while stirring up the mud of a person's life, do not offer real help. The term "sin" does not exist in their vocabulary. While trying to untangle the web of repressed conflicts, they themselves are repressing man's biggest problem, his separation from God.

Guilt and sin, however, are realities. To cover them up or

to deny them is not only unwise but dangerous. Guilt and sin are like sand in the finely tuned gears of our body. Once it is recognised, it must be removed in order to avoid its consequences. This was expressed by King David when he sang in a psalm: "When I kept silent, my bones wasted away, through my groaning all day long. For day and night your hand was heavy upon me; my strength was sapped as in the heat of summer."[30] If you are not ready to face your guilt and let Christ take care of it, you are avoiding the most important condition necessary for God's healing work to occur.

We should not restrict our conception of sin to lying, stealing or committing sexual sin. All those apparent wrong doings are in reality the consequence of man's original sin: his mistrust and open rebellion against God. All sins, small or big, really have their roots in the old, old question: Did God really say...?

Jesus once gave a universal definition of sin. He said He would convict the world of guilt, in regard to sin, "because men do not believe in me."[31]

This sin is not only committed by people living without God; often Christians do not trust God and therefore doubt His power and goodness. So many Christians walk through life as if they had never heard of the One who gave the invitation: "Come to me, all you who are weary and heavy burdened, and I will give you rest."[32]

Although God has promised that He will care for us; although we know that the Lord is our shepherd, and we will lack nothing - we still do not come to the Lord with our worries - small or big - and the dark, threatening struggles of our lives. We would rather spend sleepless nights in brooding, our thoughts going round in painful circles with no escape.

Bitterness and resentment fall into the category of unrepented sin. Although God forgives us all our guilt and shows us so much patience, it seems so difficult when we are the ones who must do the forgiving. We become like the servant in the Biblical parable who, after having a huge debt cancelled, goes out and has a fellow servant jailed for a petty amount he owed him. Why is it that we so often hold a grudge and are unwilling to forgive?

An example of what we do to ourselves through lack of forgiveness is seen with Mrs. Vine. She is a 42-year old home-maker who suffered from depression every year when the Autumn winds swept the country. One day in church she heard the message of healing according to God's plan and after the service she came in for counselling. She had had a horrible childhood. When she was old enough, she had moved out of her parents' home and would not even greet her father.

The sermon had pushed her emotional buttons: the message of forgiveness made her aware that her grudge was separating her from Christ. After a long struggle she finally made up her mind, with God's help, to forgive her father. Six months later she came back to her pastor. "Can you imagine," she told him, "In the Autumn, I expected my depression as usual, but it didn't come back. Since I have forgiven my father I am relaxed and free!"

Her story is an illustration of the fact that it is more important to get right with God and man at any cost than to look for healing at any price. Committing ourselves completely to God will lead to a healing of spirit, soul, and, not infrequently, to a healing of our bodies as well.

The anointing with oil

James mentions a *fourth* element in God's therapeutic plan: "Anoint him with oil in the name of the Lord."

What is the meaning of this ritual? R.A. Torrey is convinced that:

> ...anointing 'with oil in the name of the Lord' was an act of dedication and consecration implying, on the part of the one anointed, a full surrender to God of his hands to work for Him and for Him alone, of his feet to walk for Him and Him alone, his eyes to see, his lips to speak, his ears to hear for Him and Him alone, and

> his whole body to be the temple of the
> Holy Spirit. And the oil itself was a symbol
> of the Holy Spirit in His healing power.[33]

Here again the focus is on commitment and sanctification rather then mere physical healing. What is a man profited if he enjoys perfect health, but loses his soul?

What is your primary focus? To be healed, or to glorify God in your life, no matter what He allows to happen to your body?

Healing the whole person

There is only one reference in the New Testament that speaks of man as a whole - spirit, soul and body. Paul prays: "May God himself, the God of peace, *sanctify* you through and through. May your *whole spirit, soul and body* be kept blameless at the coming of our Lord Jesus Christ."[34]

According to the Bible, healing of the whole person is not limited to curing physical and emotional problems. *Wholesome, well rounded medicine leads a patient back into a meaningful and growing relationship with God.*

The so called "holistic" medicine is not wholistic in the Biblical sense. Yes, its practitioners do use the channels of the mind to influence the body and its functions. However, when psychosomatic diseases are treated with mere techniques, conventional or unorthodox, without taking their spiritual origins into account, the treatment merely scratches the surface. And it is here where holistic health proves to be empty, "hollowistic" rather than wholistic in the Biblical sense.

As Christians, can we expect "miracles" from therapies based on teachings which contradict the gospel, and so often prove to offer hopes that remain unfulfilled?

In the Bible we are shown the way to real, all-encompassing healing. Jesus offers us "life in its fullness". If you have accepted Him as your Lord and Saviour, not only does disease lose its terror but also death its sting. He, the Lord is sovereign, and we know that everything that happens to us is allowed by Him.

When our eyes are opened to these truths, the pursuit of health is no longer of primary concern. Rather we learn to pray from the depth of our hearts what David said in the eternal words of Psalm 23:

> The Lord is my shepherd, I shall lack
> nothing.
> He makes me lie down in green pastures,
> He leads me beside quiet waters,
> He restores my soul.
> He guides me in paths of righteousness
> for his name's sake.
> Even though I walk
> through the valley of the shadow of death,
> I shall fear no evil, for you are with me;
> your rod and your staff, they comfort me.
> You prepare a table before me
> in the presence of my enemies.
> You anoint my head with oil;
> my cup overflows.
> Surely goodness and mercy will follow me
> all the days of my life,
> and I will dwell in the house of the Lord
> for ever.

1-3 Medical criticism, Bio-Boom, Occult Revival

I am sure that any observer of our society would be able to find ample evidence for the cultural phenomena described in the introductory chapters. This is why I deliberately chose not to give specific references here. Watch the world around you, talk with people, browse through newspapers and books, get a feeling for our modern-day atmosphere, and you will find for yourself what is only sketched in my few observations.

4 Acupuncture

1.   All about acupuncture, *Newsweek*, Aug 14, 1972
2.   ibid.
3.   Bruegge P., Stich in den Punkt der goettlichen Gliechmut, *Der Spiegel* 8 (1976)
4.   Thorwald J., *Macht und Geheimnis der frueher Aerzte*, Munich 1962, p.228
5.   Duke M., *Acupuncture*, New York: Pyramid House 1972, p.67
6.   Huard P., Wong M., *Chinese Medicine*, New York: McGraw Hill 1968
7.   Thorwald, p.226
8.   ibid., p.230
9.   Schnorrenberger C., *Chen-Chiu - Das neue Heilprinzip*, Freiburg (Germany) 1975, p.83
10. Thorwald, p.229
11. ibid, p.230
12. Schmidt W., Moeglichkeiten des Nachweises der Existenz der Meridiane, *Deutsche Zeitschrift fuer Akupunktur* 4 (1969) p.109
13. Eder M., *Taoismus*, in: *Die Religion in Geschichte und Gegenwart*, Vol. VI, pp.616-19
14. Lyall L., *Confucianism*, in: Anderson N. (ed), The world's religions, London 1975, pp.219-27
15. Granet M., *Das chinesische Denken*, Munich 1971, p.274
16. Schnorrenberger, p.72

17. Ohsawa G., *Acupuncture and the philosophy of the far east*, Los Angeles (no year given) p.9
18. Granet. pp.272ff
19. Eder, loc.cit
20. ibid
21. Bischko J., *Einfuehrung in die Akupunktur*, Heidelberg 1976, p.13
22. Uccusic P., *Naturheiler*, Geneva 1978, p.239
23. Schnorrenberger, p.54
24. ibid., p.99
25. Ohsawa G., *The book of judgement*, Los Angeles (no year) p.14
26. Jia Yi Jing, quoted in Mann F., *Acupuncture - cure of many diseases*, London 1978
27. Bonin W.F., *Lexikon der Parapsychologie*, Bern/Munich 1976, key-word: Prana
28. Duke, p.59
29. ibid. p.130
30. Bischko, p.19ff
31. Stiefvater E.W. *Praxis der Akupunktur*, Heidelberg 1973, p.33
32. Duke, p.140
33. Bischko, p.42
34. Schnorrenberger, p.86
35. deTymowski J., *Indikationen und Grenzen der Akupunktur*, in: Zweiter Weltkongress der Naturheilkunde, Gossau (Switzerland) 1977
36. Hussey H., Acupuncture: Failure to relieve deafness, *JAMA* 228 (1974), p.1578
37. Schwarz R., *Heilmethoden der Aussenseiter*, Reinbek Rowohlt Publishers 1977, p.36
38. Bischko, p.13
39. ibid, p.22
40. Fisch G., *Akupunktur*, Stuttgart: Fischer 1973, p.109
41. Edelberg R., *Electrical properties of the skin*, in: Brown C.C. (ed.), *Methods in psychophysiology*, Baltimore 1967
42. Martin J. et. al., Mechanisms of palmar skin resistance and skin potential. *Psychological Bulletin* 65 (1966), p.347-57

43. Kellner G., quoted in Bischko J., op.cit., p.24
44. Schnorrenberger, p.64
45. Schmidt, op.cit
46. Stiefvater, p.23ff
47. Pongratz W. et. al., Elektro-Akupunktur-Analgesie bie 500 herzchirurgischen Eingriffen, *Anaesthesiologische Praxis 13* (1977), pp.19-32
48. Meltzack R., Wall P.D., Pain mechanisms: a new theory, *Science 150* (1965), pp.971-79
49. Kerr F.W.L., quoted in: Pongratz, op.cit
50. Mayer J.D. et.al., Antagonism of acupuncture analgesia in man by the narcotic antagonist naloxone, *Brain Research 121* (1977), pp.368-72
51. Pomeranz B., Acupuncture analgesia: endorphin implicated, *Life Sciences 19* (1976), pp.1757-62
52. Das Placebo ist ein Medikament, *Medical Tribune* Nr.1 (1979)
53. Levine J. et.al., The mechanism of placebo analgesia, *Lancet* Nr. 8091 (1978), pp.654-57
54. Wall P. d., An eye on the needle, *New Scientist*, Aug 20, 1972, pp.129-31
55. Wall P.d., Acupuncture revisited, *New Scientist*, Oct 3, 1974, pp.31-34
56. National Academy of Sciences, *Acupuncture anaesthesia in the People's Republic of China*, Washington1976
57. Kritik an der Akupunktur, *Schweizerische Aerztezeitung 61* (1980), issue Nr. 49
58. Galloon S. et.al., Akupunktur Analgesie, *Deutsches Aerzteblatt 13* (1977), pp.879-80
59. Herget H.F. et.al., Akupunktur-Analgesie: fuer offene Herzoperationen, *Selecta 39* (1975)
60. Bonica J.J., Therapeutic acupuncture in the People's Republic of China - implications for the American medicine, *JAMA 228* (1974), pp.1544-51
61. Fisch, p.8
62. Walker B., *Hindu World*, London 1968, keyword: Kundalini
63. Motoyama H., *Chakra, nadi of yoga and meridians, points of acupuncture*. The Institute of Religious

Psychology, Tokio 1972

64. Reichenbach K., *Der sensitive Mensch und sein Verhalten zum Ode*, Stuttgart 1854

65. Ostrander S. and Schroeder L., *Psychic discoveries behind the iron curtain*, Englewood Cliffs N.J. 1978, p.200 ff

66. Schnorrenberger, p.49

67. Krippner S. and Rubin D. (ed.), *The energies of consciousness*, New York 1974

68. Watson L, *The Romeo error: a matter of life and death*, London 1974

69. Carron H. et.al., Complications of acupuncture, *JAMA 228* (1974), pp.1552-54

70. Tod im Nadel-Wirr-Warr, *Der Spiegel* 31 (1975)

71. Schnorrenberger, p.121

72. Bruegge, loc.cit.

73. Duke, p.164

74. Colossians 2:8-10, NIV

5 Reflexology

1. Berkson D.T*he Foot Book: Healing the Body through Reflexology*, New York: Barnes & Noble Books 1977, p.9

2. Marquardt H. *Reflexzonenarbeit am Fuss*, Heidelberg 1978, p.88

3. Marquardt J. *Reflexzonentherapie der Fuesse*, in: Zweiter Weltkongress der Naturheilkunde, Gossau (Switzerland) 1977, p.64

4. Marquardt (1978), p.22

5. Berkson, p.7

6. ibid, p.5

7. Marquardt (1978), p.65

8. Berkson, p.2

9. Marquardt (1978), p.66

10. Berkson, p.11

11. Masafret H. *Gesund in die Zukunft*, Vaduz (Liechtenstein)1975, p.7

12. White G.S. quoted in Marquardt (1978)

13. Marquardt (1978), p.64

14. Fussmassage: Kult von gestern, *Der Spiegel* 14 (1979), p.240

15. Kibler M. Die Behandlung innerer Erkrankungen von den Head'schen Zonen aus, *Deutsche Medizinische Wochenschrift* 12 (1949), p.372-74

16. Teirich-Leube H. *Grundriss der Bindgewebsmassage,* Stuttgart 1974

17. Kohlrausch W. Gundlagen der Reflexzonen-massage, *Die Therapiewoche* VI, 19/20 (1955/56), p.468-71

18. Krause D. and Utke R. in: Luederitz B (ed.): Zur Wirkungsweise unspezifischer Heilverfahren, Stuttgart 1972, p.101ff

19. Kohlrausch A. in: Grober J. and Stieve F.E. (eds.) *Handbuch der physikalischen Therapie,* Vol II/I, Stuttgart 1971, p.180

20. Uexkuell T. *Grundfragen der psychosomatischen Medizin,* Reinbek 1976, p.166

21 Marquardt (1978), p.53

22. Pokorni T. A different approach, in: *SCP-Newsletter* VI (1980) 2, p.2-3

23. Masafret, p.69-72

24. Krippner S. and Rubin D. (ed.), *The Kirlian aura,* Garden City N.Y. 1974, p.155

25. Koch K. *Christian Counselling and occultism,* Grand Rapids MI: Kregel Publishers 1965

26. Greber J. quoted in Seibel A. *Gemeinde Jesu - endzeitlich unterwandert?* Wuppertal-Elberfeld 1978, p.180

6 Homoeopathy

1. Fritsche A. *Hahnemann - Die Idee der Homoeopathie*, Berlin 1944, pp.235-37
2. Hahnemann, S. *Organon of Medicine*. Sixth ed. Translated by William Boericke. New Delhi: B. Jain Publishers (n.d.)
3. Fritsche, loc.cit.
4. Gumpert M. *Hahnemann - die abenteuerlichen Schicksale eines aerztlichen Rebellen und seine Lehre der Homoeopathie*, Berlin, 1934
5. Tischner, R. *Das Werden der Homoeopathie*, Stuttgart 1950
6. Gumpert, p.122
7. Shealy, N. *Occult medicine can save your life*. New York: The Dial Press, 1975
8. Mendelsohn, R.S. *Confessions of a medical heretic*. New York: Warner Books, 1979
9. Gumpert, p.130
10. ibid., p.179
11. Fritsche, p.226
12. Gumpert, p.73
13. Schwarz, R. *Heilmethoden der Aussenseiter*, Reinbek bei Hamburg: Rowholt, 1977, p.74
14. Gumpert, p.73 ff
15. ibid., p.131
16. Kent, J.T., *Repertory of the homoeopathic materia medica*. Richmond CA: North Atlantic Books, 1979
17. Gumpert, p.204
18. Schwarz, p.74
19. Lagutt, J.K. *Der Grundstein der Freimaurerei*, Zuerich 1957, p.112
20. Ward, quoted in Boehme P.H. and D.E. Ressel: *Masonry in the light of the Bible*. St. Louis MO: Concordia Publishing House 1969, p.14
21. Koch K. *Der Aberglaube*, Berghausen, p.42
22. Fritsche, p.264
23. ibid.
24. ibid., p.263
25. ibid., p.264

26.   Voegeli A. *Der Angriffspunkt der Hochpotenzen,*
         Zeitschrift fuer Klassische Homoeopathie III, 3 (1959)

27.   Vithoulkas G. *Homoeopathy: Medicine of the new*
         man, New York: Avon Books 1972, p.43

28.   Randeira J.P. *Die Wirksamkeit der Homoeopathischen*
         Therapie, in: Zweiter Weltkongress der
         Naturheilkunde, Gossau (Switzerland) 1977

29.   Angerer J. quoted in Prokop, op.cit.

30.   Perry, I.E. *The Zodiac and the salts of salvation.* New
         York: Samuel Weiser Inc. 1980

31.   Uccusic, P. *Weturheiler.* Geneva 1978, pp.222 f

32.   *Der Homoeopathisierungsbegriff bei Rudolf Steiner,*
         Tagung 1974, Bornach (Switzerland), 1975

33.   Medizinische Sektion der Freien Hochschule fuer
         Geisteswissenschaften Goetheanum (ed.).
         Anthroposophie und Medizin. Dornach (Switzerland),
         1963, p.96

34.   Gauss, F. *Wie finde ich das passende Arzneimittel?*
         Heidelberg, 1977

35.   Kent, J.T. *Lectures on Homoeopathic philosophy.*
         Richmond CA: North Atlantic Books, 1981, p.211

36.   Uccusic, pp.222 ff

37.   Koch, K. *Occult ABC.* Literature Mission
         Aglasterhausen Inc. (Germany), 1980, p.188

38.   Lipross G. *Logik und Magie in der Medizin* Munich,
         1969, p.127

39.   Prokop, O. and Prokop, L *Homoeopathie und*
         Wissenschaft. Stuttgart, 1957

40.   Donner, F. quoted in Prokop, O. (ed.)
         Medizinischer Okkultismus. Stuttgart, 1977, p.201 ff

41.   Lipross, p.128

42.   Prokop, O. (ed.). *Medizinischer Okkultismus.*
         Stuttgart, 1977, p.207

43.   Netter P., Der Placebo-Effekt, *Muenchner*
         Medizinische Wochenschrift 119 (1977), 7, p.203-208

44.   Balint M., *Der Arzt, sein Patient und die Krankheit,*
         Stuttgart 1976

45.   Medizinische Sektion, p.106

46.   Hahnemann, paragraph 288

47.   Brauchle, O., *Die Geschichte der Naturheilkunde in*

    Lebensbildern, Stuttgart 1951, p.358
48.   Koch K., *Christian Counselling and Occultism*, Grand Rapids MI: Kregel 1965
49.   Bolte J., *Von der Pendelforschung zur Wunderheilung*, Eigenverlag 1976, p.12
50.   Kirchner G., *Einfuehung in die Radiaesthesie*, Genf 1977, p.218
51.   Bolte, p.81
52.   ibid.
53.   Koch (1965)
54.   Popp F.A., Wirkmodelle der Homöopathie. *Deutsches Journal für Homöopathie* (1985), Bd. 4, Heft 3.
55.   One example is an article by Reilly et al.: Is homoeopathy a placebo response? *The Lancet*, October 18, 1986, 881-886.
56.   Reilly, op.cit. 55, p.885

7 Iridology

1   Peczely I., quoted by O. Prokop, *Medizinischer Okkultismus*, Stuttgart 1977, p.36
2.   Garre, quoted by O. Prokop, op.cit., p.37
3.   Huard P., Wong M., *Chinese Medicine*, New York: McGraw Hill, 1968
4.   Prokop O., *Medizinischer Okkultismus*, Stuttgart 1977, p.37
5.   Libra, quoted by Prokop, op.cit.
6.   Jensen B., interview in *"Ravs from the Rose Crab"* (Journal of the Rosicrucian Fellowship) May 1978
7.   Schreck E., quoted by Prokop, op.cit
8.   Prokop, op.cit., p.47
9.   Woehlisch E., Ignaz von Peczely, das Eulenauge und das Mysterium der Irisdiagnostik, *Deutsche Medizinische Wochenschrift* 82 (1957), p.970
10.   Prokop, op.cit., p.47
11.   Simon A. et.al., An evaluation of Iridology, *JAMA* 242, 13, p.1385-89
12.   Jaensch P.A., et.al., Irisdiagnostik - eine

augenaerztliche Kritik, *Buecherei des Augenarztes*, Heft 22 (1965), p.30

13. Koch K., *Occult ABC*, Literature Mission Aglasterhausen 1980, distributed by Grand Rapids International Publications, P.O. Box 2607, Grand Rapids MI, p.103

14. ibid

8 Radiesthesia

1. Pohl, G. *Erdstrahlen als Krankheitserreger*. Diessen (Germany), 1932

2. Krysiak, St. Die schaedlichen Erdstrahlen. *Schweizerische Zeitschrift ueber Radiaesthesie-Geopathie-Strahlenbiologie (RGS)* 86 (1968), pp.180 ff

3. Koennen Erdstrahlen koerperliches Geschehen beeinflussen? *RGS* 140/41 (1977)

4. ibid

5. Krysiak, loc.cit

6. Comb, A. The art and science of dowsing. *East/West Journal* October 15, 1975

7. Pfuetzner, H. Die Forschung konnte das Phaenomen der Wuenschelrute noch nicht klaeren. *RGS* 134 (1976), pp.293 f

8. Janssen, W.F. The gadget quacks. *FDA Consumer*, February 1977.

9. Prokop, O. *Medizinischer Okkultismus*. Stuttgart 1977, p.98

10. Janssen, op.cit

11. Tansley, D.V. *Radionics*. In: *The visual encyclopedia of unconventional medicine*, by Ann Hill (ed.) New York: Crown Publishers Inc. 1979

12. Boadella, D. *Orgone Therapy*. In: *Visual encyclopedia*, op.cit

13. Tansley, Radionics

14. Bird, C. *The divining hand: The 500 year-old mystery of dowsing*. New York: E.P. Dutton, 1979

15. Comb, loc.cit

16. Prokop, p.87

17. ibid, p.90
18. Gassmann, F. Quoted in Schwendimann, H. *Pendel und Rute - Aberglaube oder Wissenschaft*, Valzeina (Switzerland) 1978
19. Reimann, W. *Wuenschelrute und Pendel*. In: Prokop, op.cit., p.119
20. ibid
21. Die geistige Haltung beim Pendeln. *RGS* 131 (1976), pp.72 ff
22. Mano, P. *Strahlende Welt*, Zuerich, 1949, p.38
23. Tansley, D.V. *Medical radiesthesia*. In: *Visual encyclopedia*, op.cit
24. Comb. loc.cit
25. Schoell, A. Verfuehrer greifen nach uns. *Offensive* I (1979), Bensheim (Germany)
26. Hunt, D. *The psychic war*. Unpublished manuscript, p.190
27. Eccles, J. Quoted in Rhine, L.E. *Mind over matter*, New York, 1970, p.389
28. Hunt, op.cit
29. Greber, J. Quoted in Seibel A. *Gemeinde Jesu - endzeitlich unterwandert?* Wuppertal-Elberfeld, 1978, p.39
30. Matthew 7:21
31. Nee, W. *The spiritual man*. New York: Christian Fellowship Publications Inc. 1968, Vol 3, p.30
32. Schwendimann, H. *Pendel und Rute: Aberglaube oder Wissenschaft?* Valzeina (Switzerland) 1978, p.45
33. 1 Samuel 28:6-7; Acts 16:16
34. Hunt, D. *Spiritual Counterfeits Projects Journal*, Interview. Berkeley CA: Winter 1980-81
35. Tansley, Medical Radiesthesia
36. Kirchner, G. *Einfuehrung in die Radiaesthesie*. Geneva (Switzerland) 1977, pp.200 ff
37. Koch, K., *Occult ABC*, Grand Rapids Ml, *p.188*
38. Bolte, J. *Von der Pendelforschung zur Wunderheilung*. Eigenverlag 1976
39. Koch, loc.cit
40. Hosea 4:12
41. Leviticus 19:31

42. Deuteronomy 18:9-12
43. Matthew 24:24
44. Matthew 7:22-23
45. Schwendimann, p.71
46. Zechariah 10:2
47. Michah 3:11
48. 2 Thessalonians 2:9

9 Herbal Medicine

1. Griggs, B. *Green pharmacy: A history of herbal medicine*. New York: The Viking Press, 1981, p.327
2. Thorwald, J. *Macht und Geheimnis der fruehen Aerzte*. Munich 1962
3. Huard, P. and Wong, M. *Chinese Medicine*. New York: McGraw Hill, 1968.
4. Lewis, W.H. *Medical Botany - Plants affecting man's health*. New York: Wiley 1977, p.372
5. Jacobi, J. (ed.) Paracelsus - Lebendiges Erbe. Zurich 1942
6. Jung, C.G. *Alchemical Studies*. Princeton N.J..: Princeton University Press, 1965, p.118
7. Jung, p.119
8. Lewis, pp.4 ff
9. Painter, N. et.al. Diverticular disease of the colon: a deficiency disease of western civilisation. *British Medical Journal*, May 22nd, 1971, p.450
10. Haensel, R. *Medical plants and empirical drug research*. In Swain, T. (ed.) *Plants in the development of modern medicine*. Harvard. Harvard University Press 1972
11. Ingrasci, R. and Englender, C. Caution: Herbs may be harmful. *New Age Journal*, April 1981, pp.23-24
12. Vogel, A. *Der kleine Doktor*. Teufen (Switzerland), 1977
13. ibid., p.455
14. The term "magic" is used here in the strict sense of the definitions given in the authoritative *Encyclopedia of Occultism and Parapsychology*,

edited by Leslie A. Shepard (Detroit: Gale
Research Co., 1978)

15. *Rudolf Steiner and the Anthroposophical Society.*
Spiritual Counterfeits Project, Berkeley CA, 1977

16. The most respected and comprehensive theological
encyclopedia of religion, *Religion in Geschichte und
Gegenwart,* second edition. Vol. 1, column 368, says
this: "Anthroposophy, the science of man, or
spiritual science, as it calls itself, is the most
comprehensive system of occultism."

17. Hemleben, J. *Rudolf Steiner.* Reinbek (Germany):
Rowholt 1977, p.23

18. Davis,S. Waldorf Education. *New Age Journal,*
March 1978, pp.54-57

19. Hemleben, p.134

20   ibid, p.102

21. Steiner, R. *Geisteswissenschaft und Medizin.* Dornach
(Switzerland) 1961

22. Wolff O., *Anthroposophisch orientierte Medizin und
Ihre Heilmittel* Arlesheim (Switzerland), 1977, p.40

23. Medizinische Sektion der Freien Hochschule fuer
Geisteswissenschaft Goetheanum (ed.).
Anthroposophie und Medizin. Dornach (Switzerland),
1963, p.96

24. *Heilmittelbereitung auf der Grundlage kosmisch-
irdischer Rhythmen,* Arlesheim (Switzerland), n.d..

25. *Medicine Wheel Herbal Products,* Catalogue 1982

26. Bellhouse, E. *Vita Florum.* In: *The visual
encyclopedia of unconventional medicine,* edited by
Ann Hill. New York: Crown Publishers Inc., 1979

27. *Exultation of Flowers.* In: *Visual encyclopedia,* op.cit

28. Weeks, N. *Bach Flower Remedies.* In: *Visual
encyclopedia,* op.cit

29. Messegue, M. *Von Menschen und Pflanzen.* Ulm
(Germany) 1978, p.82

30. Koch, K. *Occult ABC.* Literature Mission
Aglasterhausen Inc. 1980, p.186

31. Uccusic, P. *Naturheiler.* Geneva (Switzerland) 1978,
p.226

32. ibid., p.227

33. Kirchner, G. *einfuehrung in die Radiaesthesie*. Geneva (Switzerland), 1977, p.218
34. A helpful book is Dian Dincin Buchman's *Herbal Medicine - The natural way to get well and stay well*. New York: Gramercy Publications Comp. 1980
35. Nolen, W.A. *Healing - A doctor in search of a miracle*. Greenwich, Conn.: Fawcett 1974

10 Mysterious Phenomena

1. Steigleder, G.K. *Dermatologie und Venereologie*, Stuttgart: Thieme, 1975, p.283
2. Das Placebo ist ein Medikament. *Medical Tribune* 1 (1979)
3. Netter, P. Der Placebo-Effekt. *Muenchner Medizinische Wochenschrift 119* (1977): 203-208
4. Schindel, L. Placebo und Placebo-Effekte in Klinik und Forschung, *Arzneimettelforschung 17* (1967): 895
5. ibid
6. Levine J. The mechanism of placebo analgesia. *Lancet* 8091: 654-657
7. Brauchle, A. *Die Geschichte der Naturheilkunde in Lebinsbilbern*. Stuttgart, 1951, p.365
8. Nolen, W.A. *Healing - A doctor in search of a miracle*. Greenwich Conn: Fawcett 1974
9. Stokvis, B. and Pflanz, M. *Suggestion*, Basel 1961, p.111
10. Jores. A. *Magie und Wunder in der Medizin*, Stuttgart, 1959, p.135
11. Stokvis, loc.cit
12. Jores, loc.cit
13. Bristol, C.M. *The Magic of believing*, New York, 1972, p.14
14. Jores, p.137
15. 1 John 4:1-2
16. Matthew 9:22
17. Bender, H. Glaubensheilung und Parapsychologie. In:*Magie und Wunder in der Heilkunde*. Stuttgart, 1959

18. Bentov, I. Kundalini casualties. *New Age*, March 1978
19. Wright, J.S. *Der Christ und das Okkulte*, Wuppertal, 1974, p.41
20. Alexander, B. Holistic health from the inside. *Spiritual Counterfeits Project Journal*, August 1978, p.16

11 The Message of Holistic Health

1. Alexander, B. Holistic health from the inside. *Spiritual Counterfeits Project Journal*. Berkeley CA: August 1978
2. Alexander, B. (under the pseudonym Otto Zeit). *The coming world religion*. Spiritual Counterfeits Project (SCP), Berkeley CA, n.d.
3. Staehelin, B. *Urvertrauen und zweite Wirklichkeit*. Zurich 1973, p.157
4. Planetary Initiative for the World We Choose, *Organisation Manual*
5. Alexander, *World religion*.
6. Matthew 24:24
7. Duke, M. *Acupuncture*. New York: Pyramid House, 1972, p.164
8. Alexander, *Holistic health*, p.2
9. Alexander, D. *The New Medicine*. Berkeley: SCP, n.d.
10. Voegeli, A. Der Angriffspunkt der Hochpotenzen. *Zeitschrift fuer klassische Homoeopathie*, Vol.3 (1959) p.124
11. Hunt, D. *The psychic war*. Unpublished manuscript.
12. Keel, J. *The eighth tower*. New York: Signet, 1975, preface.
13. Means, P *The mystical maze*. San Bernardino: Campus Crusade 1976
14. Uccusic, P. *Naturheiler*. Geneva (Switzerland) 1978, p.142
15. John 14:6
16. Acts 4:12

17.	Jeremiah 2:13
18.	Keel, p.16
19.	Berkson, D. *The foot book: Healing the body through Reflexology*. New York: Barnes & Noble Books, 1977, p.8
20.	Genesis 3:5
21.	1 John 1:5
22.	John 3:16
23.	Uccusic, p.214
24.	Alexander, *New medicine*
25.	Beer J. Quoted in Prokop, O. *Medizinischer Okkultismus*, Stuttgart 1977, p.38
26.	Klopfenstein, C. *La Bible et la santé*. Paris, 1977, p.234
27.	Hebrews 9:27
28.	Vivekenanda, N.D. Quoted in Hoppenworth, K. *Neue Heilwege aus Fernost - Hilfen oder Gefahren?* Bad Liebenzell, 1978, p.124
29.	Lorenz, K. *Die acht Todsuenden der zivilisierten Menschheit*. Munich (Germany): Piper, 1973
30.	Tournier, P. *A doctor's casebook in the light of the Bible*. New York: Harper and Row, 1960, p.52
31.	Glasenapp, H. *Das Inienbild deutscher Denker*. Stuttgart 1960
32.	Alexander, *Holistic health*, p.9
33.	Mitchell, E. Quoted in Alexander, *Holistic health*.
34.	Michaud, J. Esoterische Medizin, Medizin von Morgen. *Zweiter Weltkongress der Naturheilkunde*, Gossau (Switzerland) 1977, p.198
35.	Alexander, *Holistic health*, p.24
36.	Jones, M.E. *Occult philosophy*. Boulder, Col. 1977, p.110
37.	Richter, H.E. Erst kam Hanussen.. *Der Spiegel* 9 (1974) Italics mine
38.	Rossdorf, f. Quoted in Prokop, O. *Medizinischer Okkultismus*. Stuttgart, 1977, p.38
39.	Revelation 17:2
40.	1 Timothy 2:5

12 Healing at any price?

1. Wesiack W., *Grundzuege der psychosomatischen Medizin*, Munich 1974, p.95
2. 1. Corinthians 13:12
3. Romans 8:22-23
4. McMillen S.J. *None of these diseases*, Westwood N.J.; F.H. Revell Co. 1963
5. Tournier P. *The healing of persons*, New York: Harper and Row, 1965, p.5
6. Wesiack, loc.cit
7. Laubach F., *Krankheit und Heilung in biblischer Sicht*. Wuppertal, 1976, pp.23-24
8. ibid
9. Torrey R.A., *Divine Healing*, Grand Rapids, 1977, p.63
10. Matthew 18:8
11. 2. Corinthians 12:9
12. 2. Timothy 4:20
13. 1. Timothy 5:23
14. Stott, J.R.W. *Baptism and fullness: the work of the Holy Spirit today*, Downers Grove: IVP, 1976, p.97
15. Scorer, G. In: Vale, J.A. (ed.) *Medicine and the Christian mind*. London: Christian Medical Fellowship 1975, pp.45 ff
16. Jacobi, J., ed. *Paracelsus - lebendiges Erbe*, Zurich 1942
17. Tournier, P. *A doctor's casebook in the light of the Bible*, New York: Harper and Row, 1960, p.28
18. Isaiah 38:21
19. Isaiah 38:16-17
20. Ecclesiasticus 38:1-8, *The New English Bible*. Oxford University Press, 1970
21. Tournier, Casebook, p.57
22. Jeremiah 17:5,14
23. Tournier, Casebook, p.52
24. Colossians 2:8-10
25. Blumhardt, J.C. *Seelsorge*. Munich, 1968, p.76
26. 1. Corinthians 10:14 - 11:1
27. James 5:14-16

28. Ephesians 5:20
29. Phillippians 4:6-7
30. Psalm 32:3-4
31. John 16:9
32. Matthew. 11:28
33. Torrey, p.22
34. 1. Thessalonians 5:23